GW00374899

This book is dedicated to the memory of Jim Arthur, who was an inspiration to all believers of traditional British greenkeeping and natural golf.

"A Natural Course for Golf" compiled by Malcolm Peake.

First published in 2005 by the STRI St Ives Estate, Bingley, West Yorkshire BD16 1AU, England.

Copyright © Malcolm Peake and The Sports Turf Research Institute 2005.

All rights reserved. No part of this publication may be reproduced, stored in a retrieval system or transmitted in any form or by any means, electronic, mechanical, photocopy, recording or otherwise, without the prior permission of the copyright owners.

ISBN: 1873431619

Acknowledgments

Writing this book would have been impossible had it not been for the contributors, Jon Allbutt, Tim Brooke-Taylor, Barry Cooper, Kerran Daly, John Duncan, David Garland, David Golding, Chris Haspell, Tom Mackenzie, David Oatis, Jeff Perris, Donald Steel, Bob Taylor, Peter Thomson, Peter Wisbey, Terry Wogan, and Philip York.

A Natural Course for Golf has taken over three years to compile, and particular thanks goes to Jim Arthur, Alistair Beggs, and Keith Duff for their chapters, continuous support, enthusiasm, and advice.

I am deeply grateful to Greg Davis for his considerable help in editing the book, and to David Abbott, and Martin Gunn, for their contributions, also to Sally Radford and Sue Lee who were patiently responsible for the typing

The wonderful photographs are individually credited, but particular thanks to Matthew Wellings for his specialist shots, and to Chris "Ozzy" Osborne for his witty cartoons. The chapters by Peter Thomson, and Donald Steel were edited from "Classic Golf Links of Great Britain and Ireland," published by Cassell and Co.

Thanks go to Neil Hayward, of the English Golf Union and especially to Steve Isaac, Assistant Director - Golf Course Management The R&A, for his support and for his chapter The Last Piece in the Jigsaw. Golfing charities will benefit from the sale of "A Natural Course for Golf".

Finally I must thank Sir Michael Bonallack for his generous foreword, also for the support of three great British golfers Mickey Walker, Nick Faldo, and Colin Montgomerie.

Lastly appreciation to all those unsung Greenkeepers and Golfers who share the philosophy of this book.

Malcolm Peak

Bourne End on Thames 200?

Contents

A Natural Course for Golf
Compiled and Edited by Malcolm Peake

Contents

Illustrations

Sir Michael Bonallack

Micky Walker .... Titleist

Colin Montgomerie .... Mark Newcombe (Vision in Golf)

Nick Faldo .... Renaissance PR

Malcolm Peake .... Matthew Wellings

Royal Cinque Port GC .... RCPGC Archives

St Andrews .... Steve Isaac

Royal County Down .... Royal County Down Archives

Cypress Point .... Nick Leefe

Peter Thomson, The Open 1955 .... Peter Thomson

Cartoon "In his dreams!"..... John Ireland

Bobby Jones at Royal Liverpool ..... Temple Archives

Cartoon "This is better than grass on the farm.".... Chris Osborne

St Andrews .... Toro

Cartoon "Could you leave your brains outside".... Chris Osborne

Alwoodley Golf Club .... Alistair Beggs

Cartoon "You can't close the course".... Chris Osborne

Temple Golf Club 4th Hole .... Matthew Wellings

Cartoon "The green committee is coming".... Chris Osborne

Gleneagles .... The Gleneagles Hotel

Cartoon "That must be the Chairman of Green".... Chris Osborne

This club allows the President .... Matthew Wellings

Someone is always out to get you .... Matthew Wellings

Royal Dornoch .... Royal Dornoch Archives

Cartoon "Exam in progress .... Chris Osborne

Ballybunion ..... Ballybunion Archives

The Berkshire GC .... Matthew Wellings

Illustrations

Foreword

By Sir Michael Bonallack OBE

In all probability it would seem that Golf began as the most natural of any other sport or game.

Folklore would have it that the first golfers were shepherd, who while passing their time looking after their sheep, would hit either stones or sheep dung with their crooks and bet with each other as to who could "hole out" in a rabbit hole in the least number of strokes. The links land on which they played was sandy soil, sparsely covered with fine grass that was only suitable for grazing their animals and even the early bunkers were made by sheep, scraping hollows in the sand to provide shelter from the wind.

As the game spread and went inland it was inevitable that less sandy soils would form the base for these courses, with more lush grass providing an acceptable playing surface, even if it lacked the feel of closely grown fescue.

Sir Michael Bonallack

The lay outs of the courses owed more to nature than to the skills of an architect, with the design and length of the holes being decided by natural features and contours. Indeed, it is often said that God is the greatest architect.

We have of course come a long way since those early days, but to my mind the most enjoyable and the most memorable courses are those that have been designed and subsequently cared for by people who recognize the importance of nature and all it has to offer. If you are playing badly, at least you have the consolation of the benefits of a walk through attractive surroundings, made so by the blending of golf with the flora and fauna found in that particular area.

There is no finer example of such a course than that at Temple where Malcolm Peake has so successfully preached the gospel to the entire membership and where he has been so well supported by such a knowledgeable and efficient greenkeeping team.

Not every club is so lucky! Go into many golf clubs and you will find that if the club has five hundred members, then there will be five hundred expert golf course architects and greenkeepers. Many clubs elect a number of these onto a committee charged with instructing the Head Greenkeeper how he should look after the golf course. A quick visit to the gardens of many of these committee members will quickly illustrate how ill equipped they are for such a role. The best clubs are usually run by benevolent dictators, who are the only people to whom the Head Greenkeeper is answerable.

Equally no club should allow a member or greenkeeper to make alterations to the course unless the advice of a fully qualified golf course architect has been sought.

We are very fortunate that the game has so many real experts covering all aspects of the game, who can provide the proper advice to ensure that whilst we can take advantage of the benefits of modern technology. Including new varieties of grasses and course machinery, we can at the same time preserve all that is best about the game, to ensure that it is still close to being the natural game that those shepherds played over five hundred years ago.

This book has been compiled by Malcolm Peake, who has managed to draw together the collective expertise and humour of so many people highly qualified in their own fields, but whom all have one thing in common. The love of the game of golf.

I highly commend it to all golfers.

Endorsements

By Mickey Walker OBE

Lady Golf Professional

Mickey was a highly successful amateur golfer, who won the Ladies British Open Amateur in 1971 and 1972, and the English Ladies in 1973. As a professional she won 6 European Tournaments, was Solheim Cup Captain from 1990 to 1996, coach to the Curtis Cup Team 1994 to 1998, is now Consulting Editor for The Lady Golfer and commentates on golf for Sky TV.

"As someone who is still in love with the game of golf, having played it for nearly forty years, I applaud Malcolm's efforts to encourage Course Managers, Green Committees and golfers to get courses back to their natural state. I grew up being taught golf by my Scottish 2 handicapper father, Julian, who learnt his golf on "natural" Scottish courses. My father is largely responsible for my liking of golf courses built on land that nature created and that were looked after in as organic a way as possible. In last year's glorious summer I had the opportunity to play at Rye in Sussex and was delighted to play on its brown, hard and dusty fairways. What a delight to have to use one's imagination and judge the roll and bounce of the ball when approaching a green! Nowadays most modern courses succumb to the target golf concept, which originated in America. It requires less skill to hit a ball from a lush, grassy fairway, than a rock hard, grassless one, so most inexperienced and new golfers understandably prefer the former. In part it is what golfers are used to, what they play on when they go on golfing trips to warmer

Mickey Walker, a believer in natural golf

climates and what they see on television. They don't understand that trying to create something that isn't natural in our British climate can only lead to dissatisfaction in the long run.

The other thing that strikes me is that in Britain we live in a world which is increasingly impatient and wants instant results. If a club has taken the decision that it wants to return to as natural a state as possible and for the most part dispense with chemicals, it will take a number of years, not weeks to get back to that state. Also any course in Britain is at the mercy of our increasingly variable climate. We don't enjoy the year round "growing" weather of some of our European and American counterparts.

As a golf teacher, I am a believer in correcting the root cause of a problem and eliminating the need for compensations in the golf swing. The same could be said about the current state of a golf course. It is all too easy in this "quick fix" world that we live in to pour chemicals onto the course.

So I am in total empathy with Malcolm's perspective of going back to nature, as far as British golf courses are concerned. If this book converts just a handful of clubs to Malcolm's way of thinking, all his hard work will have been worthwhile!"

Colin Montgomerie MBE

Tournament Professional

Winner of 30 Tournaments around the world, and topped the Volvo Order of Merit an unprecedented 7 years in a row between1993 and 1999. Played with distinction in 6 Ryder Cups.

It is a great pleasure to introduce "A Natural Course for Golf " compiled by Malcolm Peake. This book contains a series of interesting and informative essays on the world of golf course management. Golf has been one of my great passions for a large part of my life and its philosophy, ethos and integrity play a critical part in the enjoyment I have derived from the game. As I have broadened my involvement with golf, from tournament professional, through design and academy business, I have become increasingly excited about some of the modern architectural ideas and particularly how these are incorporated into the increasingly important ecological debate. All of us involved in the development of the sport must balance our desire to see the game grow with the critical environmental issues.

The writers have covered many aspects of the sport that I hold dear and I believe you will find " A Natural Course for Golf" a compelling and enlightening read.

Colin Montgomerie, who has a passion for the ethos and integrity of the game.

Endorsements

Nick Faldo MBE

Tournament Professional

Europe's most successful major title winner with three Open Championships, and three Masters to his name, and more than 40 tournament victories worldwide. Nick has played with distinction in eleven Ryder Cup matches. The Faldo Series has become one of the UK's premier competitions for young golfers, and Nick is guiding the careers of promising young amateurs.

I'm not sure whether it is a pun or a double-pun; either way, Malcolm Peake's chosen title for this book, "A Natural Course for Golf", is an inspired one. Given how passionately he feels about the subject matter and the quality of contributors he has assembled, I'm sure he must have been tempted to have employed the phrase (perhaps as a sub-title) 'leave it to the experts'. Yes, many of us think we know how best to create and maintain golf courses, but if we ignore the advice of those with a wealth of practical experience and professional knowledge, then we do so at golf's peril.

A certain Augusta National takes a bit of a metaphorical bashing within these pages, albeit with good intent. In several instances the contributors talk about 'the Augusta effect' – how that famous layout's apparent lush green look and ultra quick greens have caused club members in the UK to seek similar playing conditions on their home courses (presumably without quadrupling that club's green-keeping budget!). I agree with the point that is being made, although since I am one of those players who was initially seduced into taking up the game after watching The Masters on television, I feel I should highlight a few facts in partial defence of my old friend.

Firstly, Augusta is not quite so artificial or "unnatural" as people sometimes assume.

Prior to becoming a golf course it was the site of a spectacularly colourful garden nursery; it wasn't the golfers who introduced the azaleas and dogwoods. Secondly, Augusta is located in sub-tropical Georgia: it may appear pristine and luxuriant in April but many don't realise that the club is closed for much of the year due to oppressive conditions; apart from one extraordinary week each spring the club's maintenance policy generally reflects the area's climatic conditions. Thirdly, and most relevant to the message of this publication, is this simple truth: Augusta plays its best – and invariably rewards outstanding golf – when it is firm and fast-running, not when it is soft and lush.

As a player and course designer I often find myself muttering the words, 'firm and fast'. I think the over-watering and over-fertilising of golf courses (to produce a greener, so-called 'American look') is one of British golf's biggest sins.

A liberal irrigation policy merely succeeds in dampening a course's interest and character: When golf courses are soft they tend to become one dimensional; target golf is the order of the day. By contrast, when a course is set-up (or is 'allowed') to play firm and fast-running, there is a much greater emphasis on strategy and imaginative shot-making. A player is required to think his way around such a golf course and is rewarded for making sound decisions as well as skilful play.

My definition of a 'natural' golf course is one that is in harmony with and blends into the natural character of the terrain and its accompanying environment – a course that responds to its setting, not vice versa. Typically, such 'natural' golf courses are relatively inexpensive to build and less expensive to operate than courses that are built or maintained in a forced, 'unnatural' way.

I would encourage all golfers to read and digest the wisdom that is contained in the ensuing pages. I congratulate Malcolm Peake for compiling and editing this book and applaud the Sports Turf Research Institute for its insight and publishing support.

Nick Faldo coaching a student during his Faldo Series. As far as golf course management is concerned Nick suggests golfers "leave it to the experts".

Chapter 1

A Natural Course for Golf

Introduction By Malcolm Peake
Author of "Confessions of a Chairman of Green", Temple Golf Club

Malcolm's practical experiences have been amassed since 1990 as Chairman of Green, and then Course Consultant, at Temple Golf Club. Throughout this time he visited many courses around the world, meeting Course Managers, Agronomists, Turfgrass Scientists, Golf Course Architects, and Golf Administrators. He has been Chairman of the Greenkeeping Development Committee at the Berkshire College of Agriculture, has worked with The R&A Golf Course Advisory Panel, and appeared in The R&A video *"A Course for All Seasons"*, as well as the British and International Golf Greenkeeper Association video *"Golf Course Ecology"*. He has recently been made an Associate Member of the British & International Golf Greenkeepers Association. He is the author of *"Confessions of a Chairman of Green"* and joint author of *"The Wildside of Golf"*. He is a member of Temple and Royal Cinque Ports Golf Clubs and plays off a handicap of 10.

Malcolm Peake

One of the many charms of the game of golf is that it is played in a variety of settings, on a variety of terrains, no two of which are the same. In fact, like a golfer's swing, each golf course is unique, and long may it remain so.

Golf courses are in some of the most stunningly beautiful parts of the world. In Great Britain and Ireland the choice is almost infinite. There are sheltered parks, open heaths, lonely moors, enclosed woodlands, exposed downland, and the ancient links by the sea where golf has its roots.

All golfers have an opinion on the golf course, be they the club rabbit or a tournament tiger. They believe they know about the golf course and how it should be managed, but do they really?

A Natural Course for Golf will help the golfer understand course management techniques and issues. It will fuel informed debate and prevent criticism through ignorance (we have all heard sweeping statements made in the bar after a weekend medal). It will explain the different types of golf, the American target version and the natural British method, as well as the differing approaches to the management. It should increase confidence in the Greenkeeping team. One hopes it will also help golfers understand the financial and environmental consequences of inappropriate construction and maintenance techniques.

Ironically, most of the problems on the golf course are created by the very people who would benefit most from a well-managed golf course, namely **GOLFERS**. Golfers want what they see to be perfection on the golf course every day. They see it on the television and read about it in the papers and glossy golfing magazines, so why can't they have it on their own golf course? Fundamentally natural greenkeeping produces the best golfing turf at the lowest cost. Golf Clubs can't afford the high budget "Green is Great" golf course. It's an often heard misconception that golfers

Royal Cinque Ports Golf Club typifies a classic links golf course. It is being restored to its heritage, by a committed club management and a dedicated greenkeeping team.

believe that the golf course needs plenty of water and fertiliser and that pesticides can solve any problems. In addition, the course should be manicured to perfection. Golf clubs that do apply excessive water, fertiliser and pesticides are promoting softer surfaces, and coarser shallow rooted grasses which are less drought, wear and disease-resistant and produce poorer golfing turf. This is not a sustainable way to manage a golf course and it results in spiralling maintenance costs and a decline in playing quality.

My hope is that after reading this book the reader will be more likely to make a realistic appraisal of a Golf Club's circumstances and perhaps become a useful member of the Green Committee. I should know because I was that very same opinionated, unrealistic, impatient golfer back in 1990 when I first became involved. My education is far from complete, but if I don't have the answer to a problem, I know someone who does, and most of them are contributing in this book. Unknown to the average golfer, they are, nonetheless, some of the most respected people in the Golf Course Management world, and for this reason alone are worth listening to. They are a formidable assortment of experts: administrators, agronomists, drainage and irrigation consultants, ecologists, golf course architects, golfers amateur and professional, greenkeepers, and scientists.

United by a passion for real golf and natural golf courses, they have given their time and drawn upon their years of experience. They are all part of a jigsaw, which, when all its parts work together, will help a golf course to reach its potential. Application of this philosophy will conserve and enhance our priceless golfing assets, and keep the natural beauty, integrity and character of the Royal and Ancient game.

I hope it will help golfers understand what is realistic for **THEIR GOLF COURSE**, and make the job of the Course Manager just that little bit easier.

Chapter 2

The Essence of Golf – A Tournament Professional Golfer's Perspective

By Peter Thomson, CBE
Five Times Open Champion

Peter Thomson is remembered as the father of Australian golf. He won The Open five times, his most memorable victory in 1965, when he beat Palmer, Nicklaus and Player. Later in his career he became a course designer, golf writer, and correspondent. Thomson promoted golf in Australia and the Far East, and is a great ambassador for the game of golf. Peter Alliss wrote of Thomson, "He is one of golf's supreme champions and life's great companions. He is a champion to stand comparison with any before or since."

St Andrews - The Old Course has every reason to be the original course

The origins of golf are lost in the mists of time. There is little argument that it all happened in Scotland. Playing a ball game over links territory is definitely Scottish and no other.

The evidence is all there for all to see. The turf of the Old Course at St Andrews is the same piece of sward that entertained whatever humble sport took place as long ago as the 16th century. Happily it has survived untouched. The Old Course has every reason to be the original course.

Being the original course, it therefore follows that all other courses are copies, at least to fundamentals. Why else would we settle for 18 holes in the middle of Australia, or the mountains of America, or the swamps of Florida? Why, indeed, do we go to the trouble of building sand bunkers far from coastlines, if they are not in imitation of those made by nature at St Andrews?

The copies vary widely, even enormously, from the master print. Of thousands of new courses that are being built today, few have followed anything like the principles of St Andrews. There are many reasons for this. In most cases, the land is not conducive. In others though, layouts that pass for courses are no more than caricature: absurd creations that attempt to take the game into some supposedly new orbit. Such apologies distort the dimensions of a tried and noble sport. Indeed, *golf is in some peril of being led down the garden path!*

It is timely and important therefore to remind ourselves of what is valuable and classic with regard to those arenas on which golf is played at its enjoyable best. Not all of golf's classic courses belong to Britain and Ireland, but there is no other place on earth where so many of high calibre exist in a pristine state. For example, it can easily be seen that almost all classic courses have basically flat greens, or at least a flat area for the purpose of holing out. This is a vitally important part of the game that is now being over-looked. Modern designers seem to have a fear of providing anything like the level of putting area. This in its turn stems from the fear that today's professional players will make courses look ridiculously easy. And herein lies a serious stumbling block.

Courses today are being put together by property developers and land sellers. In the bygone days, most courses were built by groups of enthusiastic players who wanted a new, perhaps more convenient, links upon which to play their golf. Often, the village would encourage golf on the common land (linksland if it was available). In this way, courses grew along lines that followed classic principals. Courses were designed and built to suit everybody. Courses that were practical, pleasurable, free of humbug (as Alister MacKenzie put it). Courses that looked like a golf course should!

The property developer has no such motive. His request to the course designer is to produce something that is stunning, photogenic, and something the glossy magazines will pick up and feature. Something extravagant, outrageous - even impractical. In short, something that will 'sell my land'. They like bright lids to their chocolate boxes.

No course claims to present all that is 'classic' in golf. Beauty is always in the eye of the beholder. Links courses owe more to wild nature and Mother earth. That, to many of us, is beauty itself. Another aspect of real golf that stands out is the bunkering. A bunker can be a feature of wonder if a little of nature is tempered with a small touch of a rake to formalise its presence.

My experience of playing many classic golf courses has given me enormous pleasure. The thrill of squeezing a ball against the firm turf, trying to keep it low into a buffeting wind, is something that lingers in the mind forever. It reminds me, too, that a good deal of golf is played on the ground, or least it should be. Real golf provides this. There is a lot of chipping and long putting to do. Approaches can be made with straight-faced irons, running the ball up little banks and through the shallow hollows. It is an important part of the game, alas, little understood and appreciated and now, in modern design, virtually ignored.

Many courses are treasures that, like any other items of long-term value, are under attack. Sometimes from neglect

Royal County Down – Links courses owe more to wild nature and Mother Earth

The Magnificent Cypress Point Club

or ignorance, or even from overuse, they show signs of deterioration. They need to be preserved like ancient buildings for their aesthetic beauty and grand value. For if they are not, and golf courses follow 'down the garden path', then the very essence of what the game of golf is all about will have been lost, perhaps forever.

Editor's note: I am hoping that Peter Thomson's article will help to prove that the original game of golf, or natural golf, is still the best, and that the more recent target golf is not only less fun, but also much more expensive to sustain. It is interesting to see that even the Tournament Professionals prefer the former, and that in the 2004 PGA Tour Top 100 Courses the top 10 were all constructed before 1936, including Pine Valley GC, Cypress Point Club, Augusta National GC, St Andrews Old Course,

Peter Thomson teeing off during the 1955 Open Championships which he won at St Andrews, home of golf.

Muirfield GC, Royal Melbourne GC and Royal County Down GC. Of the top 50 only 6 were constructed after 1937. Truly great professionals like Arnold Palmer, Jack Nicklaus, Tom Watson, our own Nick Faldo, Seve Ballesteros, Ernie Els and Tiger Woods, handle not only the playing, but the mind game that is natural golf.

Chapter 3

The Art of Coarse Management

By Tim Brooke-Taylor

Tim will probably always be known as one of the Goodies, and he's quite happy with that.

But radio aficionados will also know him as one of the regulars on Radio 4's 'I'm Sorry I Haven't a Clue' which won the Sony Gold award for 'Best Radio Comedy' in 2002 and 2004.

His handicap dithers between 12 and 13, but this didn't stop him making a golf series for the Discovery channel called 'Golf Clubs with Tim Brooke-Taylor' where he played 30 different courses. He is constantly praised for this programme with the dubious compliment of 'I like the programme because I can identify with the sort of rubbish you play'.

He is proud to have served as Rector of St Andrews University for 3 years where he was, in company with many great golfers, generously awarded an honorary doctorate.

Now look here. If it aint broke, don't fix it. That's what I say to these new fangled course managers - more like coarse managers in my experience. What was wrong with calling them head green keepers? Or even, 'hey you!'

Answer – Chapter 5 – Survival on the Frontline

Look I'm not asking for the impossible, but I think it's reasonable to have quick greens all the year round. Perhaps not quite so fast in Winter – but very fast in the Summer. And what's all this nonsense about removing 'thatch'. I'd like more. It looks great on my gardener's cottage.

Answer – Chapter 16 – The Grass is Always Greener

And all that rough. Why can't we have well manicured courses with lovely lakes, and a few more trees; a few willows wouldn't look out of place, or the odd redwood. Let's plant some now and they should be ready for next season, in the meantime a few well-placed leylandii would do in the short term. On the other hand I want that oak removed on the ninth. I always hit it with my second shot to the green on the par five.

Answer – Chapter 6 – Behind the Frontline

And why do we need green keepers anyway? A lot of my friends are keen gardeners and could give a hand at the weekend; some of them could even help during the week as they've been retired for thirty years or more.

Answer – Chapter 17 – No, It's Not a Miracle....

You say that some courses are so heavily used that the grasses suffer. Easy solution – cull the membership. We managed it pretty successfully with the rabbits.

Answer – Chapter 9 – What is Your Problem?

When my lawn goes wrong I just get a strong weed killer and use lots of water. Why don't we have lots of water and lots of weed killer? And a bit more fertiliser. And even less members. Oh and cheaper subscriptions.

Answer – Chapter 18 The Future....

And while I'm on about it, why, when the course is at its best, in August say, do we have to have all those little holes on the greens. Surely we should be trying to cover them with grass.

Answer – Chapter 16 - The Grass is Always Greener

And bent grass? Just don't get me going.

Answer – Chapter 15 – The Commandments of the Prophet

To see what I'm on about, just look at those lovely American courses that we see on SKY television. Why can't we have courses like that? They're beautiful. And that lovely coloured water at Augusta, it looks so good it could have been painted.

Answer – Chapter 2 – The Essence of Golf

I've come across courses where you can't even look for your ball because it's a nature reserve. I thought this was meant to be a golf course, not a nature park. Orchids are fine for Kew Gardens but not on a golf course; at least not on my golf course.

Answer – Chapter 10 – The Birds and the Bees

For some reason our course manager doesn't like to water the entire course all of the time. When I'm thirsty, I drink as much as I can. When I'm hungry I eat as much as I can, which is probably why I need a buggy.

Answer – Chapter 4 – Real Golf....

My grandfather used to say 'Push off, you stupid, little boy'. Mind you, he was getting a bit senile by then.

"In his dream's"

Natural Golf – Preserving our Golfing Heritage

by Alistair J Beggs, BSc Hons
Senior Agronomist STRI

Alistair is a Senior Agronomist with the STRI covering Northern England and North Wales. He conducts agronomy work for The R&A Championship Committee. He fills much of his free time playing golf and is a 4-handicap member of Royal Liverpool Golf Club at Hoylake. Alistair's chapter encapsulates the philosophy of this book, and I hope he will help enlighten the reader about realistic golf course management, and natural golf.

"It is of importance that greenkeepers realise that the fundamental principle of successful greenkeeping is the recognition of the fact that the finest golfing grasses flourish on poor soil and that more harm is done by over rather than under fertilising." **Tom Simpson, The Architectural Side of Golf, 1929.**

Although penned some 70 years ago by Tom Simpson, one of the foremost golf architects of his time, these words encapsulate the crisis in modern green-keeping. In an age when we know more about grasses and soils than ever before the condition of the nation's courses continues to decline because of an excessive desire to create perfection in green. Golfers are being influenced by an ill-informed media machine, and greenkeepers are assailed by a commercial world of allegedly magical potions and lotions. This has an impact not only on our

Royal Liverpool Golf Club at Hoylake: 8th tee in the first round of The Open Championship. The legendary Bobby Jones playing with Raymond Oppenheimer (President of Temple GC 1956 to 1984). After the first round he was tied with Henry Cotton, later to be Club Professional at Temple GC. With scores of 70-72-74-75 Bobby Jones won his third Open in a row. He had already won the Amateur Championship at St Andrews and went on to win the US Open at Interlachen, and the US Amateur at Merion. Thus completing The Grand Slam a seemingly impossible feat, and safe to say a record which will never be broken.

courses but also on the very fabric of the game of golf and the way we play it. The artistry and craft of the game are being anaesthetised by the production and promotion of dartboard type greens on over-watered and over-fed courses increasingly riddled with grasses more suited to feeding cattle. As a consequence, golf is no longer played on the ground but through the air, and more and more clubs are encountering problems delivering the year-round golf our climate allows and the modern golfer demands.

The time has come for the golfing authorities to provide guidelines within which our heritage can be

Cow "This is better than the grass on the farm".

preserved, and the traditions of the game restored. At the same time, British golfers need to be made more aware of the principles of British golf course management, the role of nature, its preclusion of any other approach, and the implications this has for the way in which the game is played. *Editors Note:* **This paragraph needs reading again! It highlights the current problems, and Alistair will now discuss the possible reasons for them and some potential solutions.**

The origins of golf lie on the windswept links of Scotland where a combination of infertile soils and harsh climatic conditions made the land of little use for any other purpose. Nature's hand revealed impoverished grass swards amidst sprawling dunes which were gradually moulded and mellowed by the elements to form the ideal terrain for the game. Greens and tees were simply located on appropriate flat areas of ground, and the erosive process, started by the weather and aided by golfers and sheep, led to the development of sand bunkers. The popularity of the game dictated the move inland, often to sites that were less well suited to the game. Here, heavier soils and poor natural drainage were commonplace and restricted play to the drier months of the year.

It was nature, rather than man, that dictated turf condition in those early years – indeed it was not really until 1906 in Horace Hutchinson's book "Golf Greens and Greenkeeping" that man's involvement was first discussed. Over the years, the hand of man in golf course management grew, as did his expertise. By 1930 however,

Alister MacKenzie, the famous golf course architect, wrote "Now, alas, most of these old seaside courses have been ruined by well-intentioned but injudicious efforts of their green committees to improve upon nature." The negative influence of man had begun!!

It must be appreciated that although our knowledge and skills have improved, **nature still has the final word** with regard to what can be achieved on any golf course in the UK. It is essential to work with nature — accept what nature has given us and try to maintain a harmonious relationship with it, rather than creating artificiality at great expense and then having to perpetuate it at even greater cost. Natural golf, or real golf as you may wish to call it, is a product of a natural site managed in a natural manner. This is as true for parkland and woodland sites as it is for heathland and links. However, where the ground is less well suited to the game, appropriate management is so very important if the correct playing characteristics are to be provided.

Where these characteristics do not occur naturally we now have the knowledge to manage in a way that encourages them. Why is it, therefore, that so few clubs seem to fulfil their true potential, the condition of their courses fluctuating from one extreme to another in the face of **changing committees and changing focuses of emphasis?** The reasons are numerous.

There is an enormous influence exerted on every golfer in this country by the media (TV in particular) and its coverage of the show business that is professional golf. The initial aim of popularising the game during the 1960s

The Old Course at St Andrews has minimum use of water and fertilisers and no pesticides.

certainly worked, but it is now in danger of helping to destroy the traditions of the game in this country. It is quite ironic that those who now take the time to speak out against it are Americans themselves: Tom Watson, Ben Crenshaw and Tiger Woods, to name but three.

The advent of granular fertiliser and pop-up irrigation systems allowed the production of soft, green putting surfaces and allowed golf course environments to be manipulated far more easily. At the same time, Robert Trent Jones introduced water as a hazard on his golf courses and target golf was born. What came along with the changed philosophies of design and management was the ability to produce aesthetically pleasing arenas which colour television showed off to the full. Whilst the introduction of water hazards did not make golf any easier, the concept of soft, holding greens (target golf) certainly did. This meant lower finishing scores in tournaments, more birdies and more exciting golf.

The above scenario remains as popular today as it ever has done but whilst it is tolerable in America where golf in the main is artificial anyway, *the results of the above on natural British golf courses and their turf have been devastating* with thatch and disease ridden surfaces being closed for several months of the year. Nick Park made some interesting and very pertinent observations in a series of course maintenance articles written for Golf Monthly in the late 1980s: "I cannot see how a combination of island green bunkering, target turf and a two-piece ball has any place in a game that should be played in Britain throughout the year at a reasonable expense. It is time the authorities were able to prove or disapprove of such a statement." They still can't. He continues "We should not allow hundreds of young hopefuls to delude themselves into believing that good golf is simply a question of bashing a two-piece ball 300 yards down the fairway, hitting mechanically repeating wedges from perfect lies into a pudding, and then banging in a putt on a relatively slow green". Twenty years on this prophesy of what golf may become is strikingly close to the mark!

Understandably, the professional game has its own agenda in terms of course preparation and course presentation, and this is very different from the average club agenda. It would help if TV, which is inextricably linked with the professional game, made more of an effort to clarify the crucial differences between the objectives of the professional game and those of the nation's real golfers. If we are to see progress then an important distinction must be made between professional golf (and the courses it utilises) and participant golf, and their respective requirements. It is when the requirements of one are translated to the other that problems arise.

Over the last 20 years little has changed – indeed many may say it's got worse! PGA tour events are still largely played on courses with Poa annua greens, with the exception of the Open Championship and events hosted in warmer climates. At a time when golfers are demanding more and more because of what they see on TV, there is an ironic decline in standards because of it. TV has been great for the game, but it has been one of the principal ingredients in the decline of course maintenance quality in UK, and it continues to be influential in compromising the unique diversity and challenge of British golf.

Another possible reason for under achievement is ignorance among golfers of the traditions of course management. In the United Kingdom, we are blessed with a unique diversity of golfing sites, which golf enthusiasts the world over are fervently attracted to. ***However, the average golfers of this country do not really appreciate the quality and diversity of their courses, nor are they aware of the unique type of golf with which they are associated.*** Having been bombarded with tournament golf on tournament prepared courses, there is an expectation among memberships that they should be able to have the same. These expectations gradually permeate to committee level and, often, misinformed decisions are made. It appears that the aesthetic presentation of golf courses has become the paramount issue, and it is perceived that applying fertiliser and water in profusion, together with purchasing top of the range mowing equipment and planting exotic trees and shrubs will cure all ills and provide the ideal environment for playing the game. It won't, because such a regime cannot possibly produce good golfing conditions throughout the year. It may for short periods during the summer, but the result in winter will be closure and misery. Furthermore, the environment in which the game is played is put in jeopardy as the progression towards ecological oblivion is pursued.

There is unwillingness amongst many clubs to listen to advice that is given to them. This is apparent at both greenkeeper and committee level. The majority of clubs practice ***partial implementation of advice at best or, at worst, ignore it altogether.*** There is reticence to listen to qualified and experienced personnel because the pressures exerted by the professional game and television are strong. The results the tournament regime espouses are strikingly attractive to the golfer and are quickly achievable, and a return to traditional values will only be achieved slowly, and with heartache on the way.

Secretary to new Committee member –
"Could you leave your brains outside like the rest of the Committee."

If the desire to change does lie within our golf clubs, I am sceptical as to whether it can be achieved satisfactorily with the present structure. The green committee has changed little over the years and Alister MacKenzie, in his 1932 publication "The Spirit of St Andrews", describes concisely the problems he encountered: "We have already pointed out that it would be wise for every club to have a permanent green committee. The history of most golf clubs is that a green committee is appointed who make mistakes. Just as they are beginning to learn from the experience of their mistakes, they are replaced by fresh members who make still greater ones".

How many clubs have learnt from this and have green committees that change infrequently? For too long an individual's presence on the green committee has had more to do with personal power and ego than the long term benefit of the golf course. This will always be denied, but if the motive is not personal and is associated with benefiting the course in the long term, then relative permanence should not be a problem, because worthwhile change takes time to facilitate. What golf clubs now need are individuals with commitment and a genuine passion and enthusiasm for the game, people with sufficient humility to accept they know very little about the science, rather than people erecting monuments to their own egos and seeing how far the position will allow them to rise up the ladder to social acceptability. It is pleasing to report that in the last few years the Home Unions and The R&A have identified a lack of knowledge within clubs and committees as a weakness, and the system of practical workshops and seminars now in place for the education of Chairman of Green and Secretaries is a positive step forward.

A strong club structure alongside well-educated greenkeepers is necessary. There is often a direct correlation between the amount of money a club spends and the depth of the misery it suffers. Traditional clubs and greenkeepers continue to turn away the peddlers of potions and panaceas, keeping their consumable budgets low. Others, however, welcome them and their wares and are sucked into a vicious circle of decline at great cost! Sadly there are many that still believe their salvation lies in a packet of this, a bag of that. It doesn't – that approach always ends in tears, although it can take time to do so!

Alwoodley Golf Club, the first golf course designed by Alister MacKenzie

The bodies and individuals that give advice to golf clubs are not always innocent either. There are many out there purporting to be Agronomists who, frankly, are not. Furthermore, there is still an inconsistency of advice given (a long standing problem within this industry), from the sound to the sometimes ridiculous. In some cases this may be caused by a lack of independence – something that all clubs that take advice should insist upon. In others it may be a misguided desire to over-complicate a simple science.

So where do we go from here? Ironically, rather than change being effected voluntarily because of a greater awareness of the above issues and a desire to do something about them, it may be that our salvation will be forced upon us. European Union legislation is increasingly influencing the way we manage golf courses in Europe. The potential revocation of chemicals in the form of herbicides, fungicides, and insecticides in the years ahead will blunt the edge of commercial companies and force Committees and greenkeepers to manage in a natural/environmentally friendly manner. Those that have cultivated Poa annua greens are going to have increasing difficulty managing the problems that go with them. There will be a swing back to bents and fescues because they are the product of sensible natural management and require little in the way of artificial aid to promote them. It is sad that it takes legislation for us to question our actions and change our ways.

Legislation of a different type is being used in the US to protect certain courses. The United States Department

of the Interior has conferred National Historic Landmark status on two of America's greatest courses. Merion and Oakmont Country Club. Both have staged USGA Championships and are afforded a degree of protection as the clubs and their courses are regarded as important to the history of the United States of America. In the eyes of many, great golf courses are as worthy of protection as great art or great buildings. Future generations should be able to enjoy them as we do and the Americans have recognised this. There are many courses in the UK worthy of similar protection yet we have no system to do so. This issue surely demands further debate and thought. *Until we have such a system, the future of too many of our courses hangs in the balance and depends on the whims and fancies of memberships that are sometimes incapable of making the right choices.*

While the agenda in Europe is being forced by legislation it is important to recognise that changes are afoot and progress is being made at the highest level. Perhaps the most notable and encouraging of these is the formation of the Golf Course Committee by The R&A (www.bestcourseforgolf.org). For 250 years The R&A have concentrated their efforts on the rules of golf, the development of the game, the balls and implements with which we play it, and the successful organisation and running of some of the most prestigious championships in the world. For the first time, The R&A have identified the need for a committee devoted to course issues so that the stages upon which we play the game can receive the recognition and attention they deserve. The remit of the new committee is to address some of the issues discussed in this article and others they perceive to be of importance. It has already turned its attention to identifying areas for further turf grass research, developing advice programmes and best practice guidelines for golf course management. Is it possible that in the future The R&A, working with the STRI, the Home Unions and other independent consultants, could develop a fully funded agronomic body modelled on the USGA Green Section with a mandate to protect our golfing treasures? This could utilise the current expertise within the industry and bring it all together for the greater good of the game.

The development of seminars and workshops by the Unions was mentioned earlier. In addition to this, both the Unions and The R&A are now encouraging clubs to formulate Course Policy Documents. The development and adoption of such documents by golf clubs is a real step forward and, provided they are set up properly, they should help to protect courses from destructive fluctuations in management. However, it is a minority rather than a majority of clubs that have implemented them – there is a long way to go.

As this chapter has illustrated, the issues that have facilitated decline over the last 70 years are complex and deep-rooted. The process of effecting change has been made difficult by golfing expectation, a media intent on promoting the glory of green, and golfers who perhaps do not appreciate the traditions of the game. Change is beginning to take place, led by the most powerful body in the game. It must continue apace if British golf in the future is to resemble the game that was given to us by Mother Nature herself.

Chapter 5

Survival on the Frontline

By Martin Gunn
Course Manager, Temple Golf Club

Martin Gunn's route into greenkeeping came via horticulture. Martin was lucky enough to work for an ex-gardener from the Royal Household who was an advocate of traditional "Victorian Gardening". Martin soon found himself absorbed in a world of tropical plants, specialist fruits, ornamentals, and of course parks and gardens. He then moved on to work on sports turf, gaining experience in rugby, football, cricket, bowls and hockey. His first greenkeeping job was at Ashford manor in 1980 as Deputy Head Greenkeeper. He joined Temple in 1985 and became Course Manager in 1990.

"You Can't Close the Course- I have a match today !"

Editor's Note: It was 1990 when I first became involved in the course management of Temple Golf Club, and I did so mainly because I was a vocal critic of its condition at the time. I was a 7-handicap golfer who had taken up the game in the mid 1960's and I enjoyed and appreciated real golf. Having played in contrasting conditions in southern Europe, South Africa and America, I thought I knew about golf courses. It was not until I met Martin Gunn, the newly appointed Head Greenkeeper of Temple Golf Club, that I realised what I was letting myself in for and how little I knew about the subject. The full story of our joint experiences in change management can be found in ***"Confessions of a Chairman of Green"*** (available from STRI book dept.).

When Malcolm asked me to provide a few observations about how I (and some of my peers) view our roles in helping to produce 'the golf course', naturally, I couldn't wait.

First stop was to lobby and collect 'on site evidence' from my peers. Next, to sift through these verbal testimonies, and plan how best to explain the intricacies of green-keeping. It's not just cutting grass!

Almost immediately a pattern began to emerge as I started to encounter a few not altogether un-expected findings. For example, experience seems to indicate that often in the pursuit of sports turf excellence, a golf course fails to maximise its full potential and the original philosophy behind managing a course becomes lost.

Why this happens is the question that needs to be addressed.

After further reflection and evaluation, I decided the key is the perception at golf clubs of the role of the greenkeeper. He is mostly unseen, often misunderstood, and, perhaps most importantly, frequently undervalued. His work is hampered by internal club politics and members' personal agendas and egos, and this conflict leads to a lack of direction and continuity. Instead of having to expend precious resources in "fire-fighting", the greenkeeper should be allowed to concentrate his efforts on striving for agronomic and environmental progression, and the production of acceptable playing conditions on any given day!

I'm sure you'll agree that this scenario is a fairly difficult one in which to operate. If one adds to this the various

Temple GC designed by Willie Park Jnr the 4th hole

other compounding factors, such as variable weather patterns, climate change and legislative pressures, it seems a wonder that the industry hasn't already imploded.

As you can imagine, this can make 'survival on the frontline' a somewhat interesting experience - to say the least. In fact, the more I asked greenkeepers their opinions on this, the more I was convinced that being a greenkeeper was similar to being involved in a campaign of war. In this war one army is represented by the golfer, and sometimes even the employer – who are generally only concerned with today - and the other army is represented by the greenkeeper - who has to balance these demands with the need for measured and quantifiable agronomic and environmental development.

Often, the opening exchanges of this conflict are a series of salvos and skirmishes, which inevitably have an impact (rarely positive) on the golf course itself. One could even hypothesise that those greenkeepers who have succeeded in the past and survived their time in the industry must have some of the characteristics of the 'great generals'.

"The Green Committee are Coming"

They must have been skilled in areas such as intelligence gathering, reconnaissance, strategy, communications, logistics, diplomacy, regrouping, recovery and, of course, peacekeeping. The need for these proficiencies will be a surprise to many readers, but it appears that they are the key skills for the modern greenkeeper to have if he (she) is to produce a successful, well-managed golf course.

Why are these skills needed? Quite simply, persistent meddling from owners, members committees and even well meaning

Gleneagles – The multi-sensory experience that some golf courses offer

individuals at the decision making level can have a detrimental effect on the greenkeeper's ability to reach even the most basic of objectives. Compounding this is the somewhat puzzling notion that often, after employing the best qualified person (a Course Manger or Superintendent) to manage a golf club's most valuable asset, the employer then retains the right to over-ride decisions on even the most inconsequential detail. This is the most contentious and irksome aspect of the job for most greenkeepers.

There are further examples of poor delegation at management level within the industry, delegation that never devolves the real responsibility for making appropriate decisions. Surely, these must just be 'control freaks' I hear you cry? Well, perhaps in some cases, yes, but if those 'some cases' turn into the majority, then the industry really is in danger of having the 'lunatics take over the asylum'. It's as if the employer really doesn't have faith in those who are employed as custodians to deliver objectives or to act in the club's best interests. *This is not a very positive situation for any of those involved!*

However, for those who do manage to negotiate their way through this potential minefield, the prospects are much better. With the fundamentals of policy and continuity established, the route to maximising potential is altogether much clearer. At this point objectivity can surface and more often than not, through mediated compromise, the holistic and multi - sensory experience that golf has to offer can be explored and appreciated by all concerned.

What about the introduction of 'change management' ?

This seems to be the obvious solution, but how to achieve it requires much debate and deliberation. Along with others who have tried to initiate such strategies, Malcolm and I know that it is a very stressful, isolated and often painful route. When asked about this, one esteemed agronomist remarked, "In most cases not only do these Clubs have to go backwards before they can move forwards, the medicine they have to take leaves a very bitter taste in their mouths".

Perhaps the industry could start by evaluating the roles of a number of governing bodies involved in the game. Unless there is a unity of purpose amongst them, the industry is floored from the outset. If Golf had a central lead whose responsibility was to provide direction regarding the strategic and operational development for the entire sport, so much the better for all concerned, especially the greenkeeper!

However, in all of this there are many positives. For example, if we consider the "foot soldiers" at the centre of this issue, they are, by and large, genuinely motivated, reliable people whose vocation lies in making an honest living. Perhaps, this is something that should recognised and cherished in this era of 'status anxiety'. More importantly, if employed in a properly managed environment, these are the very people who have the potential to pay back their employer and their chosen industry many times over.

The Golf Course Manager's Lament
By Kerran Daly MG
Course Manager, The Gog Mogog Golf Club

I was just a wee bit lad o' seventeen, when first I steppit oot upon the green
I soon got goin' wi' my Ransome cutting stripes so bold and handsome
Mine were the best six greens you've ever seen.
But I don't cut the greens any more, no I don't cut the greens any more
You may find me in committee, spinning them another ditty
But I don't cut the greens any more

The boss gave me a five-minute lesson, on how to mix and spread the old top-dressin'
With a wrist flick and a fling I could make that shovel sing
'Twas the day I fell in love wi'my profession
But I don't do top-dressin' anymore, no I don't do top-dressin' any more
You may spot me oot assessin' other folks doing top-dressin'
But I don't do top-dressin' anymore

When the early summer sun began to break, you could spy me walking
oot there with my rake
Squattin' doon upon my hunkers pullin' weeds oot o' my bunkers
Cursing golfers for the mess that they a' make
But I don't rake the bunkers any more, no I don't rake the bunkers any more
You'll find me up in Harrogate as a conference delegate
'Cause I don't rake the bunkers any more

I used to be as happy as old Larry, whizzing up and doon from green to carry
I'd be oot on my machine man whistlin' 'Mr Tambourine Man'
I was the fairway king o' Ballingary
But I don't cut the fairways any more, no I don't cut the fairways any more
I'm in some meeting tryin' to hack it in my BIGGA tie and jacket
'Cause I don't cut the fairways any more

Now the boss he'd send me oot to do the tees, and I'd always do my very
best to please
I used to love that divot fillin' singin songs by Bobby Dylan
Whilst thinking on the bonnie birds and bees
But I don't sing Bob Dylan any more, no I don't sing
Bob Dylan any more
It's kinda' sad when you reflect the price we'll pay to earn respect
'Cause I don't sing Bob Dylan any more.

Chapter 6

Behind the Frontline
...The Green Committee

By David Oatis
Director North East Region U.S.G.A.
Agronomist

Green committees serve a vital role in the management of a golf course, but there is a great disparity in their relative effectiveness. There is valuable information in this chapter for any golfer who wants to serve on the green committee and applies anywhere in the world. David Oatis is Director of the North East region of the United States Golf Association Green Section. David has worked behind the front line for 16 years with the U.S.G.A on the cutting edge of developing grasses and technology, yet he remains convinced that the vast majority of turfgrass problems are caused by fighting nature. Most can be solved through good construction, suitable growing environments and sound cultural programmes, which improve the health, reliability, and playability of golf course turfgrasses.

THE TEN MOST COMMON MISTAKES AND HOW TO AVOID THEM

The United States Golf Association Green Section agronomists make yearly 2,000 turf Advisory service visits annually to more than 1,500 different golf courses during the course of each season. Visits are made to every type of course imaginable, from elite championship sites to public and municipal courses, to low-budget nine-hole facilities, and the structure and relative effectiveness of the various committees that oversee the operation of these courses vary nearly as much as the facilities themselves. Nevertheless, most of these varied courses have a few things in common. They all take pride in their facility and have a strong desire to improve it. And yes, most of the committees that guide them have the propensity to make mistakes. Just as each course has its strengths and weaknesses, so do their committees. Some are remarkably effective, while others squander funds and/or are ineffective. You might be surprised to learn that the mistakes made by Green Committees often are quite similar, both from course to course and decade to decade, even country to country.

So, Green Committee mistakes are not new, nor are the mistakes they make original. Most have been made countless times before by countless committees at countless golf courses all over the world. There is a distinct pattern to the mistakes most commonly made, and it is hoped that this effort to identify common Green Committee mistakes will help your committee avoid them.

THE ROLE OF THE GREEN COMMITTEE

Green Committees have the responsibility of overseeing the management of the golf course, but they must not be involved in its day-to-day management. Rather, they are an advisory board whose role should be to hire a golf course superintendent and make broad-based decisions on budget and policy. They need not have specific knowledge of turfgrass management, but they must understand the game of golf, have a desire to learn, and have time to devote to the process. Effective participation on a Green Committee requires a significant commitment of time and energy, and *it is not a commitment to be taken lightly.*

In charge is the Green Chairman. His task is to organize and hold regular meetings of the committee and to develop and maintain a close relationship with the golf course superintendent. At courses with problems or conflicts, this can be a most unenviable role, yet it also has the potential of being extraordinarily rewarding.

An effective chairman and committee working with a competent superintendent can develop and implement plans to maintain and make improvements in a golf course that can be enjoyed by golfers for generations. Conversely, when an ineffectual committee and a superintendent cannot cultivate a constructive relationship, it can drag the course down, creating or adding to problems, the effects of which will be suffered for years. Perhaps the simplest description of the committee's role is that *"...they must protect the golf course from the golfers!"* If the average golfer had his way, greens would never be aerated, pesticides and fertilizers would never be applied, and trees would only be planted and never removed. In truth, chaos would reign, turf would fail, and playability would be abysmal!

Being a chairman or member of the Green Committee is not a popularity contest. Tough decisions frequently must be made regarding disruptive and expensive programs and projects, and thick skin and an ample dose of conviction are required. Green committees serve a vital role, committees have many opportunities to make mistakes, so now let us review what the Green Section staff believes are the ten most common ones.

That Must Be the Chairman of Green!

TOP TEN GREEN COMMITTEE MISTAKES

No. 10 : Shopping for the Right Opinion.

"Their minds are made up and they do not wish to be confused by the facts," describes the committee that falls into this trap. Some committees look for a superintendent or consultant who will give them the answers and corresponding recommendations they desire. "Sure we can keep the greens in championship condition all season!" ..."Heck no, you don't need to aerate!"...or "we don't need to close the course for maintenance!" might be some of them. Green Section agronomists occasionally have been labeled as "the superintendents mouthpiece" by such committees. Realistically, if the opinions of the agronomist happen to be in concert with the superintendent's, it just may be because the superintendent has it right in the first place.

Turfgrass and golf course maladies often require complex, expensive, and/or disruptive solutions that every golfer would choose to avoid if given the option.

It is the mission of the USGA Green Section and of any independent agronomist to help courses devise the most reasonable and effective solutions to their problems, but cheap and easy are of little value if the solution is not effective. Sometimes, courses need to take a step back in terms of conditioning in order to take several steps forward. For instance, courses that want top-notch putting greens usually need to put up with the disruption of aeration, verticutting, topdressing, and pest management programs. *Medicine doesn't always taste good, but we still have to take it!*

No. 9 : Not Enough Time To Participate Fully.

An effective Green Committee member must put in the time! This means attending as many of the regular meetings as possible. It also means educating oneself on the subject of turfgrass management and learning specifically about issues that might be facing their individual course. Prospective committee members should not underestimate the time commitment or the effort it takes to attend meetings, seminars, and Turf Advisory Service visits, or the time it takes to educate oneself. It is also essential to spend time with the superintendent, both on the course and at conferences and seminars. Chairmen and committees also must take the time to develop open, honest relationships with the golf course superintendent.

No. 8 : Figurehead Chairmen.

The green chairman should be a duly elected course official and a voting member of the Board of Directors. The green chairman in that capacity has far more leverage and influence on the outcome of controversial issues and is a much more persuasive advocate of the golf course management operation.

Frequent turnover in the leadership position of the Green Committee is never a good idea, but it can be especially

This golf course allows the President to select and plant a tree of his choice in the location of his choosing! Planting the wrong type of tree in the wrong location creates a problem that can last for generations. An Indian Bean Tree (Catalpa bignonioides) an alien species in this environment planted too close to the green.

disastrous when it happens mid-season!

No. 7 : Micromanagement.

Green Committee members and chairmen must have a basic understanding of and a strong interest in course management programs. The committee should make broad-based policy decisions and should not be involved in the day-to-day maintenance of the golf course. The committee member also must realise that the competent superintendent has a better appreciation of the "big picture" and may have other maintenance issues to deal with that have higher priorities. (See Martin Gunn's comment in the previous chapter.)

No. 6 : Unrealistic Demands

Just about every committee wants more in terms of turf quality and playing conditions than they can afford, and some want more than is humanly possible. Perhaps it is just basic human nature, but placing unrealistic demands on the golf course superintendent, maintenance personnel, and turfgrass is an all too common pitfall. Examples include trying to maintain championship conditions every day of the year or requiring that the greens be a specific speed every day. These are problems that are often fuelled by television golf coverage. *Most of the courses portrayed each week on television are in nearly flawless condition, and this one-sided view of course conditioning gives golfers everywhere the unrealistic notion that the courses are maintained in this condition every day of the year.*

No. 5 : The Legacy.

According to Freud, all humans have egos. Based on personal experience, some egos are much larger than others and a committee or chairman with a large ego can be easily transformed into someone who wants to "leave their mark on the course." To that end, peculiar and impractical designs are sometimes contrived and perpetrated on the course, squandering labour and funds and wreaking havoc on the course. Low priority, pet projects are sometimes funded, even when there are not enough funds to purchase much-needed supplies or equipment, and this frequently occurs to the detriment of the golf course and the maintenance budget. It may also hurt the superintendent's credibility if he is forced to "go along" with an inappropriate project.

Green Committees can avoid this pitfall by utilizing and listening to competent consultants and by developing master plans for long-range improvement. Such plans often address proposed architectural changes for the golf course, but also should include the more mundane infrastructure necessities such as irrigation and drainage systems, maintenance facilities, cart paths, tree management programs, ecology etc.

No. 4 : The Inability to Make Tough Decisions.

The duties of a Green Chairman and Green Committee are not for the fainthearted. Issues often arise that require tough decisions that may raise the ire of an entire golfing membership. It should always be the goal of the superintendent and the course officials to avoid disruption of the golf course and golf schedule, but the solutions to some problems require just that. Severe soil problems may require aggressive cultivation programs. Badly deteriorated bunkers may require total reconstruction. An antiquated irrigation system may require an expensive replacement project, and playability problems and poor turf performance may require tree removal programs. Issues such as these can be emotionally charged, and the decisions will have far- reaching impacts on the viability of the course.

While a band-aid approach might be needed on a short-term basis, consistent reliance of this type of approach winds up wasting money and perpetuating problems. At some courses, *"it seems there is never enough money to do the project right the first time, yet there always seems to be enough money to do it again!"*

No. 3 : Unbalanced Representation or fails to Represent All Golfers.

Committees can be too large; of that there can be no doubt. Large committees often have difficulty staying focused and on track. They tend to have too much discussion and have trouble reaching decisions. Some have suggested that the most effective committee size is and odd number less than three, but there is a risk involved in having such a committee.

Committees that are unbalanced often fail to consider the effects their actions will have on golfers of different abilities. Green Committees should be comprised of golfers of both genders and all abilities. This helps to take different perspectives into account, and it helps to keep lines of communication open with other golfers.

No. 2 : Short Tenure.

Individual committee members spend a tremendous amount of time learning about the science of golf course management, and the experienced committee member becomes an extremely valuable resource. Superintendents typically spend a tremendous amount of time helping to educate committee members, as this is an important part of their duty. *Frequent turnover in Green Committee members produces duplication of this effort, is wasteful of the superintendent's valuable time, and can be extremely frustrating.* Frequent turnover also wastes the time and expense incurred in each committee member's educational process, and it greatly increases the odds of making those rookie mistakes. *Frequent turnover makes continuity impossible.*

No. 1 : Poor Communication Skills.

Maintaining an open and direct line of communication between the superintendent and the Green Committee is essential, and it can be difficult to achieve.

One of the more effective means of keeping committees and superintendents on the same page is specifying maintenance guidelines, *(Editor's note – A course management policy document see chapter 9 by Jeff Perris of the S.T.R.I.)* This should be mandatory reading for all Green Committee members. Assuming effective communication is maintained between committee and superintendent, the next step is to ensure that the committee communicates effectively with the Board of Directors and the golfers.

The old adage "a little knowledge is a dangerous thing" certainly applies here. Frequently, committee members try to answer complex agronomic questions and wind up giving inaccurate information that just confuses the process. Even the most experienced Green member should be quick to say, "I don't know the answer to that question, but I'll check with our superintendent and get back to you." Doing so can save a tremendous amount of embarrassment, confusion, and grief!

Committees need to communicate effectively with the golf course superintendent and with the golfers, particularly when major projects or expenditures are being considered.

Some programs are hard to sell, but Green Committees that educate their golfers, schedule meetings, and provide written documentation and access to their consultants to explain why the programs are needed, generally fare the best.

Conversely, committees that take an arrogant approach and assume the golfers will simply take their word for it, frequently experience vehement opposition and fail to gain the support of the golfers.

Being a Green Chairman or Green Committee member can be a tough job. Someone is always out to get you!

Chapter 7

Working Together

By John Duncan
General Manager Royal Dornoch G.C.

John Duncan graduated from Edinburgh University with an MA. He served in the Army and retired in 1994 as Lieutenant Colonel. During his service career he was Captain of Munsterlager Golf Club, Northern Ireland Army Golf Society and Combined Services Society, with membership at the Royal Hong Kong Golf Club. He has been Secretary/Manager of Royal Dornoch Golf Club for 10 years where he participates fully in club matches and competitions. He has been committed over a number of years to the professional development of golf club secretaries and managers and currently is on the Board of the Club Managers Association Europe.

Royal Dornoch "Generations of architects have travelled to Dornoch to worship the shrine" Donald Steel.

As both a Secretary/Manager and a member of a golf club, I can claim to be an expert in greenkeeping. That, anyway, is my experience of club members' views. However, I think I have a few additional credentials to justify answering this invitation to express my views. As a manager of a famous links I have been custodian for ten years of a valuable part of golf's heritage. Links is where golf was born. Whilst we accept to a degree that the demands of members mean we must mollify Mother Nature and thus occasionally apply water and some chemicals, that is not an excuse to change the characteristics of the natural grasses. On a links, heathland, moorland, downland, even parkland course, green is not good. The links head greenkeeper aims to provide tight lies and firm fast greens and enjoys seeing the grass a straw colour in high summer.

Much is said about modern technology spoiling the game and the need to curb innovations. However, as can be seen in tournaments when a links is prepared in a traditional manner, the nature of the links provides its own defense and few outrageous sub-par rounds are achieved.

I learnt golf on a Scottish hillside course, have played parkland, heath land, and links courses around the world. The latter two have always been my favourites. That view was fundamental to establishing a good working relationship with my head green keeper. He is of the Jim Arthur School and was relieved and encouraged to find there was a meeting of minds. I have learnt a lot from him and the way the course progresses under his regime has strengthened my faith in the prescription of traditional greenkeeping. Our relationship is in no way a master and slave one, but a team effort where our respective skills are complementary. I found it was important to make an effort to learn and understand the fundamentals of green keeping so I could appreciate the keeper's problems. I found the STRI Course at the BIGGA (British and International Golf Greenkeepers' Association) annual conference to be a good starting point, as was some basic reading. At the same time, the communication needs to be two-way and I was perhaps fortunate that, once the Course Manager was made aware of any resource constraints and other competing needs of the club, he appreciated the need for compromise or patience at times. I have made the point, and will repeat it that, in a club of 800 members there will be 800 greenkeepers. Sadly, the professional qualifications and depth of technical knowledge of the modern green keeper are rarely fully recognised by members. The Secretary - who is usually held in higher esteem - can and should protect Head Greenkeeper as much as possible.

It is necessary to add that the modern secretary needs to work at keeping that esteem. After retirement from, for example, the army, police force or bank, appointment to a golf club manager's position does not render it acceptable to rest on one's laurels for the remainder of one's working life. The proficiencies required to manage a golf club in today's environment are varied and specific to club management. Until recently there has not been an opportunity for golf club managers to follow such a route, even if there had been some evidence of desire. Now, however, the recently launched Club Members Association of Europe, modelled on the Club Managers Association of America, which promotes education and continual professional development, is attracting younger more ambitious golf club managers who seek to raise standards in their clubs.

The Secretary can contribute best to the course management through good personnel management procedures which create a contented work force. This does not mean getting involved with day to day tasks etc, but it does mean ensuring staff appraisals are conducted in a structured manner and training plans are drawn up to promote an individual's personal development. Getting the message over to committees to ensure proper funding is in place for this will tax his political skills.

The reader may note that I have used the traditional titles of Secretary and Head Green Keeper. In this day and age the correct terminology should be General Manager and Course Manager to reflect the responsibilities of both posts. Such terms make the point that both individuals are professionals and have a professional relationship.

I am aware that there are authors who hold very reactionary views on some modern greenkeeping . I worry about taking such a black and white view. I would like to suggest to the reader that golfers fall into two categories - Hitters of golf balls and golfers. The first group want target golf as they take a pride in the mechanics of hitting the ball a certain distance. They seek predictable and consistent course conditions to help them do that. They want soft receptive greens and lush fairways with grass under the ball. In other words, they want a style of greenkeeping that is anathema to the old school of advisors and green keepers, *and they should be made aware, that this method of greenkeeping is likely to be unsustainable in the long run.*

'Real Golfers', on the other hand, enjoy a style of golf in which there is a challenge through being presented with a variety of options. Such golfers are happiest with tight lies and firm fast greens. They take satisfaction from manufacturing shots and playing with feel rather than relying on club technology to hit a specific distance. Clearly my Course Manager and I favour this form of golf. In the interest of good public relations I had to bite my tongue during a recent summer when asked by a golfer for a refund because our fairways were disgusting, i.e. they were a straw colour after a glorious spell of dry sunny weather. (Editor's note: see Mickey Walker's comment in her article.) As the dry spell continued for a substantial time I will admit to sharing some doubts, which where being expressed round the club, but my Course Manager was reassuring and I trusted his judgement and backed him. In time he was vindicated when autumn rains arrived and plentiful green healthy grass was soon evident.

There will be a problem when you have both types as members in one club, but depending on whether it is a hitter of balls or a golfer who heads the green committee, the way the course is presented can swing from extreme to extreme, and that results in neither characteristic being properly met. I strongly adhere to the position that the General Manager and Course Manager must have a good personal relationship and be in agreement on what they want to achieve for the condition of the course. A lot of angst could be avoided if the professionals - General Manager and Course Manager- were allowed to manage and committees confined themselves to setting policy. However, the temptation to tinker is ever evident in club committees. Perhaps the Captain's bunker, which distracted them from causing serious problems elsewhere, was not a bad thing! It could be suggested that the best way to deal with committees is to treat them like mushrooms.......

Chapter 8

A Battle of Wits

...The architect acting as examiner and the golfer the pupil trying to fathom the answers

By Donald Steel
Golf Course Architect

Donald Steel was an International golfer and played in The Open Championship. He was Golf correspondent for the Sunday Telegraph for almost 30 years. In 1965 he joined Cotton, Pennink and Lawrie as a golf course architect. In 1987 he formed his own company and has designed 75 courses in 25 countries, and advised on scores of others. Donald has accepted the nomination to become President of English Golf Union in 2006.

Many believe our traditional links are the only true form of expression and that anything else is second best. Their love of them amounts almost to a passion. Nowhere in the world is there anything else that compares; indeed, nothing that comes close. All our great championships are contested by the sea and, happily, no change of policy can be contemplated in the foreseeable future.

There is a joyous sense of space and freedom about most seaside links, a feeling of escape that makes you glad to be alive. Only a tiny handful of golfers play purely to meet the game's essential, competitive challenge. The vase majority do so for reasons of health, exercise, exploration and the sheer enjoyment of the beauty in which they find themselves.

Golf course architects have a duty to arrange their layouts in the way they think makes best use of a particular piece of land and the best use of the budget available to them. There are a few unwritten 'rules' to which the best of them conform but there has been a growing belief among developers of new courses in recent years that so-called championship courses, a much misapplied and misunderstood term, must have a par of 72 with four par 5s and four par 3s – two in each half. That makes no more sense than regularizing the size of a potato.

Character, after all, is the most important ingredient on any golf course, the joy of links being that they are entirely natural. That is why, before architects lent a hand, they were merely adopted as they were found. What God created, man implemented. Most links have something in between, the undulations that give pockets of humps and hollows, making an even lie or stance less likely. Traditionalists jump for joy; modernists tear their hair out.

Those professionals who want everything predictable, with shot-making geared to a stereotyped level, expect perfectly straight drives to be teed up in the middle of the fairway in full view of the green and the bottom of the flag. They would prefer the term 'rub of the green' eliminated from the dictionary, but adherents to traditional links golf contend correctly that the powers of invention necessary to overcome any unexpected situation plays straight into the hands of the more gifted. Reducing everything to a common denominator brings success within the range of the many.

A Battle of Wits

Ballybunion "A course on which golf course architects should live and play before they build golf courses." Tom Watson

On American style courses, any player 120 yards short of the green will think of playing only one club – a wedge that must carry all the way to the flag. On a traditional course he may have the choice of four or five clubs and can execute the shot with every club two or three different ways. When the wind whips up on a links course he may need four or five clubs more than the day before. Winds are an almost in-built hazard, and constant change of wind direction makes some courses seem like four-in-one.

It is interesting and entirely relevant to this debate that in 1991 there were grumbles from eminent figures in American golf that US tournament courses are dull and artificial, producing a generation of young professionals less good than their European counterparts. Their argument was based on the lines that Americans are only used to playing in perfect conditions. On British courses that are less manicured, improvisation is essential. You hit the shots you can, not the shots you want. (Editor's note: A great lesson – think about it.)

There was criticism of Americans for not being innovative enough. A tough wind on a links calls for punching shots low with two or three clubs more than a yardage chart may indicate. It is no good selecting a 7-iron, hitting it into the heavens and complaining when it comes up short.

Tom Watson, who was as innovative as any, said of Ballybunion that it was a course on which many golf architects should live and play before they build golf courses, hinting no doubt that links demand a wider range of shot-making than any type of course. He was too modest to say that is why he has won the British Open five times but, if the purpose of any Open is to produce the best champion, it is unarguable that over the last thirty years the British Open has been more successful at doing that than its American counterpart. The reason? Links courses. Mighty men can be turned into midgets as the knack of flighting shots low becomes vital to survival. In these circumstances, yardage charts are not worth the paper they are written on, but as welcome as the dawn is the shaft of sunlight, in the wake of dark cloud, that signals the weather is on the mend. Tranquillity descends and all is right with the world again.

On the rare occasions when there is no wind, the ground is receptive, and the greens are putting true, links can represent the easiest form of golf but, to be seen at their sporting best, they need to be fast-running with emphasis on the low pitches, the putter working overtime from off the green – occasions when the wedge is blunted. Architects must visualise everything through the eyes of players of all standards, another way of saying they should have experience as golfers themselves.

Golf is a continuous process of decision-making, a strategic exercise that must explore the options on every shot on every hole. It then becomes a test of manoeuvrability and control, rather like a game of snooker; the more skilfully the current shot is played, the more straightforward will be the next. Architects should never ask players to embark on impossible missions – that would be too simple. Architects, for the most part, explore the fine dividing line between what is challenging and what is unfair. If players are able to unravel and knot, architects are delighted; but, if they fail, then it is a case of let the devil take the hindmost. Golf course architecture is a battle of wits, with the architect acting as the examiner and the golfer the pupil trying to fathom the answers.

Architects are fighting a losing battle against the advances in the manufacture of clubs and balls over which they have no control and to which officialdom pays insufficient heed. Changes from the feathery ball to the gutta-percha ball and from gutta-percha to the rubber-cored ball brought about dramatic shortening of holes but it is the further improvement in the ball in the last twenty or thirty years – together with little restriction on materials for the shafts and heads of clubs – that threaten the game. Unless a tight rein is kept, golf course architects may become powerless.

It may be one argument (that of The R&A in the mid-1960s) to say it doesn't matter how low scores become as long as it is the best players who produce them, but nobody wants 8000-yard courses in order to establish a status quo. What about those existing on 90 acres or so in the middle of town? They are already stretched to the last inch.

Some architects have tried to combat the trend by building modern courses that are impossibly difficult, completely losing sight of the fact that 80 per cent of all golf is played by those of more than 15 handicap. These players pleasure is paramount and losing half a dozen balls per round is not everyone's idea of fun.

Hiring household names to produce something more shocking, more spectacular, is not the answer. The highly respected and skilled band of men who, early in the 20th century, replaced the top professionals – whose designs were geometric and artificial and created the profession of golf course architecture, still have a message.

The likes of Harry Colt, Alister MacKenzie, Herbert Fowler, Tom Simpson, James Braid, A.W. Tillinghast, Donald Ross, Mackenzie Ross and Sir Guy Campbell realized that golf courses have an air of permanence and that that air of permanence depends upon a knowledge of how to build as well as how to design. In spite of a few understandable adjustments, their work has retained an incredible freshness. However, the basic truth is that a study of British and Irish seaside links remains the finest way to understand the principles of golf course architecture. These courses teach us how avenues between dunes, heather, gorse and meadow rough, reward straightness and accuracy. They show the thinking behind the placing of bunkers. They reward the virtues of positional play, which can erode the priceless weapon of power. They reveal the importance of the proper angling, shaping and contouring of greens – the ultimate centrepiece on every hole on every course. They emphasize that subtle variations of level add to the interest and appearance. Above all, they underline the vital need for architects to possess those abstract qualities you cannot teach – imagination, attention to detail and eye for land. That is what separates the good from the also-rans, the truly authentic traditional courses from others that are, at best, only thin imitations.

The Berkshire – a classic Herbert Fowler design – arguably the best 36 holes of golf in the UK

Chapter 9

What is Your Problem?

By Jeff Perris B.Sc
Director of Advisory and Consultancy Services,
STRI, Bingley

In the autumn of 1966 Jeff joined the Sports Turf Research Institute (STRI) as an advisory officer with the job of advising on the maintenance of sports turf playing surfaces. After a significant period of training and familiarisation with STRI practices and policies, he started advisory work at golf clubs. Then, after several years, he progressed to advising not only on the management of golf courses but the construction of greens, fairways and tees, etc., and this has been his vocation ever since.

However, within the first few months of his training he concluded that the education and knowledge he had acquired in plant and soil sciences was inadequate and perhaps that he should return to university and seek an additional degree in Psychology! There was no doubt that the problems he was encountering in his early advisory life at golf clubs were not just agronomic but also of a human nature. Indeed these thoughts were shared in 1989 by The R&A Greenkeeping Panel document "The Way Forward" which immediately identified that "the problems facing our courses today are more serious than at any stage in the game's history. Broadly speaking, these problems resolve into two areas: agronomic and human". For those who can access this document it is well worth reading and pondering whether things really have changed in the last 16 years.

Agronomic Aspects

These are many and varied but the main areas could be considered to be:

Course-Construction/ Upgrade

Without doubt any significant new construction or upgrade should be the domain of those who have undergone proper golf course architecture training, such as that operated by the European Institute of Golf Course Architects (www.eigca.com). There may, however, be the odd situation such as the construction of a new tee or bunker where the experience and knowledge of a golf Course Manager or Green Committee member may be sufficient for the job. I am afraid, however, that there are still too many well-meaning amateurs dabbling in golf course architecture. They are invariably ignorant of the crucial elements of landscape form, climate, soil type, drainage requirements, construction materials, environmental influences and future maintenance requirements, to say nothing of understanding the golfing aspects of strategic or penal design. The importance of not tinkering with golf course architecture cannot be over emphasised.

With regard to construction works, these should be undertaken using proven methods and materials. Where there are specific guidelines on golf green construction from the USGA or STRI, they should be fully implemented. Simply choosing any old stone or sandy type rootzone for the construction profile is perhaps one of the most frequent and misguided ways in which USGA or STRI guidelines are ignored. If one were building a clubhouse and particular materials were stipulated for a specific construction performance, I wonder how many people would deviate from those specified materials without recognising and accepting the consequences?

Pure Agronomics

This is such a huge area and well beyond the scope of my contribution. All I can do in this instance is refer readers to various works outlined in the Titles of the World booklist from STRI (www.stri.co.uk). I heartily recommend the books *"Care of the Golf Course"* by STRI, *"Practical Greenkeeping"* by J.H Arthur and *"Golf Course Management"* by James Beard. An understanding of the contents of these publications, followed by sensible operation of the principles they expound, should allow the attainment of good standards.

What Do You Mean, we need more and better staff!

OZZY

Whilst the aforementioned publications will give good general guidance to golf course maintenance, I have found, after many years of experience, that several aspects of agronomy are frequently involved in course problems. To name a few:

- The inappropriate use of irrigation to meet agronomic and golfing requirements.
- The deployment of inappropriate mowing heights in relation to growing and weather conditions. Clubs must get away from the mentality that green speed can only be achieved by very close mowing of the greens.
- The effects of trees on turf performance.
- The failure to identify the importance of cultural treatments in relation to pests and diseases.
- The use of unsuitable top dressing in relation to the specific needs of the turf.
- Insufficient thought given to controlling wear.

There are then occasional examples of structural problems which constrain agronomic performance such as:

- Inadequate resources to maintain the course properly. This will often embrace machinery and materials, and also the number and quality of greenkeeping staff.
- Lack of a course management policy which embraces short, medium and longer-term objectives.

Despite these particular concerns, I feel that agronomic problems at golf clubs have improved over recent years as a consequence of a better understanding of turf culture by greenkeepers, as well as advances in machinery and materials used in course maintenance. There are, nevertheless, a number of areas where further research is needed to fill gaps in our knowledge, and a number of new issues are appearing as a consequence of climate change, the diminishing availability of chemicals and the need to have viable alternatives. The interesting question here is who drives forward such essential research and who pays for it?

Apart from The R&A, nobody else seems interested in independent research. I feel this is a great pity as all bodies that have an obligation to the game should bear some responsibility for improving playing surfaces. The Golf Unions set aside a small sum of money from the Union affiliation fee to support the training and development of greenkeepers, which is excellent. Why shouldn't they also support an appropriate and coordinated research programme into agronomic issues?

The Human Factors

In my opinion these are the main reasons why golf courses fail to realise anything near their agronomic potential. Indeed, I would say that 80 - 90% could be improved, and in many instances this can be achieved by resolving the human issues. Such issues invariably fall under the following headings:

Greenkeepers

The Head Greenkeeper or Course Manager is in charge of course condition, development and presentation. Unless this point is understood and accepted by club committees and the members in general, then difficulties will arise. A good Chairman of Green, even with supportive committees, advice from an agronomist, input from architects and ecologists etc., is no substitute for a good Course Manager with the skills and experience to create optimum course condition.

Over the last 10-12 years through the efforts of the British and International Golf Greenkeepers Association (www.bigga.org.uk) and various education programmes, there is no doubt that the process of producing high calibre professional Head Greenkeepers/Course Managers and more thoughtful and skilful greenkeepers is well underway. There are now some excellent professional Course Managers with all the skills (practical, theoretical and managerial) that are necessary for maintaining the modern golf course. Having said this, there is still a long way to go before the supply of such high calibre people is anywhere near to meeting the demand.

Over the years, and perhaps never more so than at the present time, I would say that if there is an element of the job that lets Course Managers down it is the question of man-management. *Within man-management I include managing committees, as well as greenkeeping staff!* Course Managers must be skilful negotiators, firm when required, diplomatic, proactive rather than reactive and, above all, totally professional. Unless a Course Manager can create a perception within the golf club that he (or she) is the ultimate authority as far as golf course matters are concerned there will be problems. The pressures on Course Managers and greenkeepers today are probably greater than they have ever been, due to the demands and expectations of club members.

Club Officials

This is where I feel many problems originate and, unfortunately, are perpetuated. I am sure that all club officials and committee members take on their responsibilities intending to do their very best. Thankfully, on many occasions their Club benefits from their thoughtful and selfless contribution. Unfortunately, however, there are too many occasions when the individual input is ill-considered and selfish, with a large ego often being the guiding force. Such is human nature.

Club Committees

Apart from individual frailties and failings, it is often the club committee structure that prevents progress and realisation of potential. Again, The R&A document, *"The Way Forward"* identifies this serious constraint of committee structure affecting course standards and development. Advice was offered in the document on how to produce a much simpler and more enlightened Green Committee structure. I wonder how many golf clubs have moved towards that desirable state?

Without doubt, club and committee structure will always play an important role in golf course matters, and quite rightly so, as the course belongs to the members. Sadly, however, communications between club officials and committees often leave a lot to be desired and course matters can often be decided in an autocratic way. Relationships between club officials/committees and greenkeeping staff are often another problematic area, to the point where the Course Manager or Head Greenkeeper is not invited to Green Committee meetings. What a disaster for the Course Manager and Green Committee - but more importantly the club!

What is Your Problem?

Club Members

I would like to include some thoughts on the average club member. Within a large group one should expect a diversity of attitude, outlook and understanding. We have all heard the comment that within any club the golf Course Manager has 600 experts to advise him. This could be a sad reflection of the Course Manager's perceived ability or his failure to communicate to the members that he has all of the necessary skills and expertise to deal with course problems

I have no doubt that the best for many golf clubs is for their committees to use the "enlightened structure" suggested by The R&A in "The Way Forward" document. The club should then procure a first class Course Manager and produce a well-considered course management policy document which will form the basis of the club's course development and standards for the future.

Others Involved

Other contributors to golf course development and management range from architects, agronomists, contractors and suppliers of products. Once again their role within golf course development and management should be clearly identified, preferably through a golf course management policy document. Where possible, consultants belonging to their professional bodies should be engaged, for example, architects within the European Institute of Golf Course Architects or agronomists who are on the Register of Independent, Professional Turfgrass Agronomists (www.ripta.co.uk).

Sometimes where golf clubs require an external input from, say, an architect or agronomist they base their choice simply on cost. Indeed, some golf clubs will avoid engaging well qualified, experienced and professional consultants, when they need help, as they say they cannot afford it. My response to this attitude is that if you haven't got a lot of money it is probably more important than ever that you invest it properly. Clubs who have a lot of money can afford to correct mistakes but clubs with limited finances cannot afford mistakes or disasters.

My Way Forward

For clubs to realise the potential on their golf course, they must have the following:

- A truly professional Course Manager with all of the necessary practical, theoretical and, particularly, man-management skills.
- A club committee structure and, particularly, Green Committee structure that will support an intelligent golf course management policy.
- Good communication channels between the three essential parties of Greenkeeping staff, Green Committee and Golf Club Members.
- A strong management team empowered by the expertise of consultants such as agronomists and architects when necessary.

I live in hope that golf clubs will move towards the above ideals but I wouldn't be surprised that if I were to re-write this contribution in 20 years time I would be preaching the same message. When it comes to ignoring logic and common sense, my wife, a Yorkshire lass, invariably trots out one of her favourite sayings "there's nowt as queer as folk".

Chapter 10

A Subliminal Feeling of Wellbeing

By Bob Taylor BSc (Hons)
Senior Ecologist STRI

Bob Taylor is probably the most well-known and respected ecologist specialising in golf. His combined knowledge of the game and how this can and does interact with ecological and environmental factors is unsurpassed. Bobs ecological interests stem from his early days as a general naturalist enthused by all aspects of the natural world. He later became specialized in mycology (the study of fungi), which led him in 1986 to read Botany at Sheffield University. Bob joined the STRI in 1989 and set up the ecology and environmental services for golf. He has visited many golf clubs throughout the UK and Europe and works closely with the statutory conservation bodies. He is also ecologist to The R&A responsible for the ongoing conservation management of all the Open Championship courses. Bob runs the annual Golf Environment Competition for BIGGA that over the years has helped considerably in improving awareness within and outside the golfing industry.

One of the greatest challenges we, as a global society, are likely to face throughout the early 21st century will be in balancing human population growth and expansion whilst protecting and securing the ecological integrity of our vastly diminishing natural resources. *Golf on a local level can contribute significantly towards this challenge.* Many golf clubs are already playing an extremely important role in this respect through ensuring the long-term conservation of our dwindling countryside. Through their actions, wider recognition of the very positive role that golf courses as a major land use can play within our wider countryside is being achieved.

As the statutory conservation organisations gradually come to accept the positive influence of golf on the landscape, it may be that a major ongoing challenge for the golfing industry will be to convince golfers themselves, that "golf courses are much more than sites for playing golf". They conserve habitats and wildlife that owe their very existence to how the site is managed. Conversely, it may be the ambience created by the presence of a myriad of different flora and fauna that makes or breaks one's perception of an enjoyable and uplifting game.

There are several statements that are oft repeated by golfers:

- *This is a golf course, not a nature reserve.*
- *If I want wildlife, I'll go to a nature reserve.*
- *This course is difficult enough without more rough.*
- *Do not remove trees.*
- *Managing areas of rough will take up time needed for perfecting the putting and playing surfaces.*
- *What benefits to the golf club are likely to arise from adopting a more ecologically sound programme?*

These statements, although probably well-meaning, are generally voiced without any understanding of how the various components of the course interact and why appropriate management off the playing line can be so important.

I have endeavoured to provide answers to the above by providing some ecological background to demonstrate why certain features need to be built into any management programme and, indeed, why conservation management work is so important in ensuring a healthy environment for all involved:

"This is a golf course not a nature reserve"

Leave the golf clubs in the locker room, take a casual walk over the course and appreciate all the different wildlife types to be found. Away from the casual rabbit, the mallard duck or the tame fox, observe the less obvious wildlife and use all the senses to pick up colours, movement and sounds. The dawn chorus may include the persistent sound of the skylark - a bird that has declined significantly over the past twenty years or so largely due to habitat

The Skylark, an ordinary-looking little bird, but what an evocative song!

loss and modern farming practices. The more open coastal golf courses such as Royal St Davids in North Wales, and Royal Cinque Ports in Kent, the heathland and downland courses such as Royston in Hertfordshire supporting skylark are playing a vital role in ensuring the survival of this species for future generations to enjoy.

Bumblebees may be seen flitting from flower to flower. Normally thought to be relatively common within our wider countryside, they are under severe threat. Indeed, only six out of sixteen previously widespread species are now commonly seen. Bumblebees in search of clovers, vetches and other flowers require large areas of grassland to maintain viable populations.

Golf courses, do play an important role in maintaining a great diversity of wildlife, and this role can be extended. Expedient management (for example, cutting areas of rough during appropriate periods within the year rather than on a routine basis) would help free the greenstaff's time, allowing more time to be spent managing the more "important" playing areas. The most important parts of the course for the actual game would thus be improved whilst at the same time a more attractive area for wildlife would be created. The severity of the rough, providing appropriate management is given, need not be overly compromised – it may actually be possible to improve it, allowing easier ball retrieval and onward play.

Other species of national importance and occasionally seen may include grass snake, adder, slow-worm or smooth snake. Coastal golf courses such as Southport and Ainsdale and Silloth in Cumbria may conserve sand lizard and natterjack toad. A few such as Formby golf club on the Ainsdale coast also support strong populations of red squirrel.

The golf courses situated within increasing urbanised settings should not be seen as less important than the coastal courses lying within larger tracts of open dune land. These courses, dominated on all sides by housing, industry or perhaps intensive arable landscapes, do provide a rich, green oasis upon which great spotted and green woodpecker may be dependent. Butterflies, including the gatekeeper, meadow brown, speckled wood, ringlet and comma, may be well represented but, also, isolated, finding no scope for wider dispersal unless appropriate connecting habitat running through the suburban or arable landscapes is provided.

Thus, in summary, each "isolated" golf course will support a rich diversity of different wildlife forms. I often see golfers, having played a less than acceptable round of golf, returning to the clubhouse frustrated and irritated. Their comments however differ from course to course. Those having played on a relatively impoverished course tend to appear more disgruntled than those having walked through a beautiful setting of well-defined rough benefiting from birdsong and the associated movement of butterflies and dragonflies. Here, the response may be, ***"Not so good today but enjoyable nevertheless"*** (the comment reflecting the whole experience and not just the golf). It is apparent that not only are wildlife and golf highly compatible, the wildlife element is utterly desirable. The golfer will benefit from a subliminal feeling of well-being, induced by the ambience and beauty of the setting, whilst the wildlife will benefit from the nature reserve that is symbiotically being created.

"If I want wildlife, I'll go to a nature reserve"

There is little need if you consider and fully understand the significance of the above.

The desire for tidiness amongst golfers is a serious problem, however, and is one that the golfing industry must address and ideally overcome. ***Man has become a "control freak", striving to extend the living room into the garden and restructure the landscape in the form of a garden.*** Wildlife, however, does not recognise tidiness and has no concept of what we believe to be "nice". We must come to recognise that birds and other species don't always like "nice" places. It is a misconception that all golf courses contribute significantly to wildlife. Too many, in my opinion, manage to such an extent that wildlife is driven out. To us "people", the course may support a nice green parkland sward with a few varied evergreen and deciduous trees, designated pathways and well constructed facilities, but for birds and most other living things this landscape may as well be the Sahara Desert. It will contribute

You'll enjoy playing here: the fairways are lined with beautiful trees

little to wildlife and will, moreover, compromise the experience for the majority of able golfers. There is much truth in the words of Gerard Manly-Hopkins, ***"Oh let them be left wilderness and wet, long live the weeds and the wilderness yet"***.

Nature reserves do support some of our most endangered wildlife (as do many golf courses) but these nature reserves will never be extensive or numerous enough to safeguard the totality of wildlife represented. Furthermore, nature reserves tend to be relatively isolated and spatially separated, with minimal connectivity running between them. This can have a serious long-term impact upon species' survival. Golf courses such as

Walton Heath GC - A club with a responsible attitude to conservation management which also enhances the Golf Course

Sunningdale Old Course – The picturescue 9th Hole – Trees encroaching on the left can affect the playing surfaces and the architecture of the hole and will need to be felled.

Strensall (York) or Hesketh run alongside areas designated for their wildlife interests extending therefore out as a finger into the countryside, do, play an important dual role by increasing the overall area for wildlife providing valuable corridors of similar vegetation through which they can travel and disperse.

These ecological highways, if they are to be fully effective, must be given appropriate management to prevent natural changes from taking place. This may simply involve periodic monitoring and occasional removal of naturally regenerating trees or the management of the grasslands to prevent nutrient enrichment and a gradual change in species composition.

"This course is difficult enough without encouraging rough"

The rough that defines each hole gives definition, hole separation and, importantly, imparts penalty to the wayward shot. The degree of penalty depends largely upon the type of vegetation and the management practised. Surely golfers would agree that the aim must be to create a sward that facilitates ball retrieval and onward play, albeit with penalty. In most cases, such conditions can be achieved through intelligent management, normally carried out at a time when other more important works have been completed. Once an acceptable sward has been achieved, in many instances it will be possible to expand this zone, so allowing the semi-rough and cut rough to be brought closer into the playing (fairway) line. This will provide for stronger hole definition and a more interesting course on which to play. On golf courses such as Wilmslow for example where acceptable transitional rough is being created, it is becoming gradually possible to reduce the width of the fairways, so providing greater challenge and reward to the well struck shot. Rough grassland should not considered contentious, it should be an integral component of a course.

The wider ecological rough running out from the cut and transitional zones may require different management approaches to ensure that a greater variety of different forms of wildlife are being supported. In many instances this could result in an infrequent cut (possibly on a rotational basis so as to minimise the labour and input required) but it may also simply require periodic monitoring to prevent scrub or tree ingress.

"Do not remove trees"

The removal of any tree is likely to be met with emotive arguments and contention. Tree removal, however, can be as important for the well-being of one habitat as tree planting may be for another. Consider the decrease in area of chalk grassland or heather-dominated heathland upon which many golf courses are sited. Unimpeded natural tree invasion here will normally lead quite rapidly to a loss of these important habitats and, moreover, a loss of their associated species. Given the lack of similar land within the surrounding landscapes, any significant changes on the course could lead to a series of gradual extinctions. the Skylark, although quite mobile, does depend upon open grassland and cannot tolerate trees of any kind. Without management, trees will gradually encroach, leading to the loss of this important bird species. On many courses, heather is being lost as woodlands push ever outwards toward the playing-line. Trees, through shade, leaf drip and needle and litter deposition, will gradually reduce the extent and quality of the heather. Bear in mind that it may have been just these features that early golf architects/ developers were keen to include in their original designs.

Even on the parkland golf courses a lack of management could lead to a rapid change in the woodland/grassland condition. A number of courses support woodlands designated as ancient in origin with significant numbers of veteran trees. Here, the ingress of shade-tolerant species such as sycamore could result in a loss of the native woodland condition. These trees, being quick-growing and light-demanding, can cause a premature senescence of the more established and more important trees.

Alien and exotic trees may have a place on certain courses but one must always consider the reasons for choosing these trees over possibly more suitable species. It may be that they give year-round colour or have other desirable aesthetic attributes, but will they offer through the longer term the kind of protection, screening or featuring which often forms the principal reason for their introduction? Many courses including Alwoodly and Pannal in Yorkshire and Tandridge, Gerrards Cross and Beaconsfield in the south of the country work towards a phased tree removal/replanting programme, placing emphasis on the gradual removal of alien and exotic species to ensure that internal/external protection is not compromised and a more stable and less resource-demanding landscape is provided.

"Managing areas of rough will take up time needed for perfecting the putting and playing surfaces"

In most instances the opposite is true. With appropriate management it is possible to improve the quality of the rough with relatively infrequent attention. It is often the case that club officials fail to recognise areas that could be developed as rough using very few resources. Simply by raising the cutting height, possibly introducing some infrequent scarification work, and ensuring litter collection is undertaken, these areas may form acceptable and aesthetically pleasing golfing rough.

I find it ironic that golf clubs will spend inordinate amounts of time and resources strimming around trees and Flymo'ing tee bankings but roll out the statement above when faced with carrying out some non-intensive management work to perfect the quality of the wider rough. Surely, if any golf club requires more time in perfecting and managing the putting and playing surfaces, then this will inevitably entail a reduction of the unnecessary intensive management operations carried out elsewhere.

In summary, recognising the areas that need to be intensively managed for the playing of the game, and those that don't, will allow the greenstaff to direct and prioritise management work more effectively - if this differentiation is recognised within a structured long-term management programme.

"What benefits to the golf club are likely to arise from adopting a more ecologically sound programme?"

Managing with wildlife in mind has given greater credibility to the golf industry. No longer is golf seen as selfish land use, a game for the privileged few; it is increasingly being seen as a conserve of valuable habitat, a whole series of interconnecting nature reserves. Indeed, enlightened conservationists are realising that golf courses are vital for the ongoing protection and conservation of some of our most endangered wildlife. The favourable change in public perception of golf courses should benefit individual golf clubs themselves. Improving the wider rough will improve a club's prestige, making it a talking point, and a reason for returning time and time again.

Appropriate management will help by improving course definition and providing strategic and visual interest on each golf hole. An ecological approach will allow the greenstaff to give more time to improving the quality of the putting and playing surfaces through a redirection of available resources. Adopting a conservation management plan should lead to better communication with the statutory and non-statutory conservation organisations which, in turn, will lead to a better working relationship, benefiting both golf and wildlife. The principal benefit to golfers is be able to play golf in a setting of such abundantly diverse natural beauty that enormous pleasure can be derived no matter how badly one is playing.

By redeploying resources, golfers will enjoy improved playing surfaces as the greenstaff will be able to spend more time managing those parts of a course which clearly require a more intensive management approach. On most courses the greenstaff waste considerable amounts of time cutting and managing areas well out of normal play. This is an expensive waste of, machinery, labour and time.

The greenstaff also benefit significantly from managing with wildlife in mind, principally from having greater motivation, satisfaction and direction; new skills and a more efficient and structured daily routine. In addition, clubs like Temple in Berkshire, Moortown in Leeds, or Silloth in Cumbria have received substantial grants for ecological management projects.

Summary

The challenges facing the world over the next twenty to fifty years or so are huge. One of the greatest hurdles will be to reconcile the prevailing environmental changes with human population growth. The hurdles that the golf industry face may at times seem insurmountable, particularly where intractable, opinionated course management committees and ecological/ environmental issues collide. Golf and wildlife, nonetheless, can benefit from one another and the implementation of good ecological practice will lead to major benefits in terms of time management, additional resources, and greater access to funding and advice. On top of this, playing golf in a beautiful natural landscape that has been ecologically enhanced by being a golf course must surely bring pride to any golfer

Golf clubs considering managing "through the green" would be best advised to assess and survey thoroughly the types of habitat and predominant species present as this will inform the suitability of different types of management. Once a strategy has been agreed it is essential that a longer-term management plan is produced which ensures that a phased, practical approach is adopted (this will be key to ensuring ecological sustainability in the longer term). Such a plan is important for it ensures that the programme continues well beyond the next change in committee. A management plan should offer a series of recommendations or prescriptions, providing time scales and methodologies and must give cognizance to the needs and objectives of the game. Failure to recognise the need for proper management will lead to a progressive deterioration in the areas "left for wildlife". The consequence of this will be not only a decline in the wildlife but also in the playing condition of the course.

And then one would be back to square one…

Michael Parkinson and his comments from the Wildside of Golf. "The royal and ancient game of golf continues to give pleasure to millions of golfers worldwide. Played on a wide range of courses from parkland to seaside links, the game can be challenging and frustrating but also satisfying, allowing players to take part in gentle exercise in delightful surroundings. Many golf courses are wildlife havens contributing to the preservation of landscapes and the conservation of habitats and wildlife, whilst catering for the needs of the golfing fraternity."

Chapter 11

It's Alright for the Tournament Professional

By David Garland
Director of Tour Operations,
PGA European Tour

David Garland joined the European Tour in 1988 as a Tournament Administrator, becoming Tournament Director in 1990 and Director of Tour Operations, his present position, in 1997. His role is responsible for all Field Personnel of the European Tour including the Agronomy Department.

He is a keen golfer playing off 2 handicap at Wentworth GC and Elie in Scotland, and is a member of The R&A.

The majority of golf clubs and courses never get the opportunity to host a European Tour Tournament and, as such, there are a number of misnomers about the Tour and course conditioning, the set-up of the golf course and its 'agronomy/ greenkeeping' support staff. I hope this article will clarify the situation for the golfer.

One of the strengths of the Tour is that it plays on a variety of different types of courses, links, heathland, parkland and many new, modern creations. All over the world each is treated uniquely, as every one has different grasses and a different climate, so the 'set-up' of the courses is different.

Our aim is for the golf course to provide a tough, fair challenge for the Tour professional who are some of the best players in the world. To assist the club in achieving this, we do have 'course preparation guidelines' and we do have an 'agronomy/greenkeeping' support team who work with the resident course staff.

Before discussing our guidelines further, I would firstly like to state that our 'agronomy' department is there to assist the Course Manager and staff.

Our personnel do not take over the running of the course.

We advise and support as much as we physically can to ensure the best possible playing surfaces. This might mean our staff being on-site for a couple of weeks (though we have had instances where staff have been on-site for 10 weeks).

(Editor's note: Only superficial improvements can be achieved in this timescale.)

Through our contact with Toro, the official supplier to the Tour, we are able to support the venue with additional machinery. While via our association with Bernhard we can send in a mechanic and grinding technician to ensure all machines are cutting perfectly and at the exact heights.

Putting Greens get the greatest scrutiny and criticism of any area of the course (just like at your own course). In our guidelines we have three main criteria. In order of priority they are:

1. Smoothness of putting surface which will allow a ball to run straight and true without 'snaking' or 'bobbling' and remain in contact with the surface at all times.

2. A good green will be firm (not hard) and will accept a well-struck iron shot and will reject a poorly struck approach shot or a shot from the rough.

3. Pace of the greens should be as fast as possible, *provided that the surface smoothness is never sacrificed in order to produce speed.* Obviously each venue will vary in pace depending on putting green construction, grass type, machinery available and climatic conditions. But speeds between 9'6" and 11' are desirable.

As you see, we are not ruled by the stimpmetre! Yes, we do have venues where the greens run faster than 11' but only if the quality of the surface can take it. *Our guidelines highlight top dressing, aeration, verticutting and water control to achieve the desired quality, just as it should at your own golf course.*

Regular light dressings of approved dry sand, well matted in, will assist in giving a smooth surface for the ball to run on. The increase in number of cuts of the tournament green will also help the roll of the ball on the greens.

Wentworth Andrew Oldcorn on his way to victory in the 2001 PGA Championship

In some circumstances the use of rollers (such as a Turf Iron) can aid the leveling of the putting surface but care should be taken not to negate pre-tournament aeration by over-rolling.

Firm and fast greens provide the best test for both approach shots and putts. A sound programme of using as little water as necessary can help produce championship greens and a well-struck medium iron from the fairway should be able to grip and hold. (The desired effect lies in a layer of thatch or fiber no thicker than 10mm).

The great tendency is for clubs to over-fertilise and over-water too near to the event, which apart from creating growth promotes the build-up of thatch. Green (colour) is not always best. Apart from not rewarding the skilful well-struck shot, soft greens tend to footprint and mark.

Ideally the green conditions and speed at the beginning of the tournament week should be nearly identical on the final day.

We do not stipulate a cutting height for greens, as much care needs to be taken to ensure they are not put under much stress by too much cutting at low heights, particularly when tournaments are played at sensitive times, i.e. spring, autumn or periods of excessive heat. The frequency of cut during an event can vary greatly, from double cutting to six times between rounds. Again the programme is agreed between the Course Manager and the Tour, normally the Tournament Director, and will change daily if required. Hand mowing or cutting by triplex are both acceptable to the Tour.

We do ask that the direction of cut is changed for every cut to help reduce nap or grain.

Naturally any treatment that the greens undergo should also be applied exactly in the same way to the practice putting green.

For the most part, **COLLARS AND APRONS** should be treated as the greens. It is useful to have the cutting heights the same as the tees (i.e. 8-9mm) as generally the same mower is used to cut both. It is important, however, that the apron is cut in a diamond pattern and that the collar is

cut in reverse direction each day to prevent the build up of nap.

The collar width guideline is 1.2m (1.3yds) and that this should be maintained at this width around the entire outline of the green.

In the weeks prior to the tournament and even during the practice rounds, the championship **TEES**, especially Par 3 tees, should be rested.

Tees should be level, firm and maintained at a height of 6-8mm. It is very easy for championship tees to become soft through lack of play and lack of aeration. This must be monitored.

In the event of strong winds, or purely to give variety, the Tournament Director may request that a couple of teeing grounds on a particular hole are prepared ready for play.

Tees should be cut in a diamond pattern as a tee cut directly towards a fairway can be misleading to the line of play.

FAIRWAYS should be between 22-32 metres in width depending on the difficulty of the hole. If a course is being used for the first time, the Tournament Director may narrow or reshape the fairways in line with the distances the professionals hit the ball.

The fairways should be cut at a height of 8-12mm. Fluffiness in fairway turf is undesirable and the tendency should be towards firm, tight turf.

Mowing heights for tournament play should be established one to two weeks in advance, as last minute reductions in mowing heights create excessive loose grass cuttings on the fairways and could cause 'yellowing' and scalping.

But whenever possible boxes or grass collectors should be used. Small hollows should be hand-cut if fairway mowers cannot produce a uniform surface and all loose grass should be removed. Small hollows should be leveled, if possible, prior to the tournament.

Wherever possible, all fairways should be cut in the morning prior to play, boxing the clippings off. Where it is not possible to obtain boxes, it may necessary to cut some or all fairways after play and in this instance we would require fairways to be swept before play (normally by dragging a hose pipe) to remove dew.

Ideally all fairways should be cut in a diamond pattern, with regular reserve cutting to prevent nap.

The long stripe cutting pattern or half light and half dark pattern favored by links courses are acceptable.

Whatever mowing pattern is chosen, reverse cutting is vital to stop nap, as on thatchy, soft fairways nap does affect the striking of the ball.

The Tour does and will implement the preferred lies rule if it feels it is necessary. In the majority of cases, it is only introduced if the ball is 'picking up' mud, as the flight of the ball is adversely affected when struck.

A complete programme of divoting should be carried out at leased four weeks prior to the tournament.

Around the fairways there should be a strip of semi-rough 3-4metres wide, which should be cut at a height between 25-35mm. All semi-rough should be cut in the same direction.

The height of **ROUGH** will vary depending upon whether or not it is maintained, and the type of grass.

If any new sand is required for the **BUNKERS**, it should be applied at least two months in advance of the tournament so it can become well settled.

We prefer that bunkers are maintained by hand and are raked in the direction of play.

Two areas that are vital to the success of the tournament but are sometimes overlooked are:

The **PRACTICE AREA**. This is where the modern professional spends hours and hours. Therefore the teeing area should be prepared in the same way as those areas on the course and is required to be a minimum of 10m deep to accommodate seven days of practice.

RAIN PREPARATION. Many believe the tour follows the sun but I can assure you the Tour ends droughts when it arrives in town! The course must be prepared for the worst.

In concluding, I must stress our aim is to have the best quality playing surfaces possible week in week out, venue to venue, and this can be achieved only by working very closely and in tandem with all the host venues' staff.

A well-presented course in first-class condition benefits all parties involved in the Tournament.

Editor's note: David's article is an insight into the fascinating world of tournament golf. But readers must remember that these standards are not possible or even desirable week in week out at most members golf clubs.)

Chapter 12

The Architect Conducts but the Contractor Plays the Music Construction, Drainage and Irrigation

With assistance from Jim Arthur, Barry Cooper Donald Steel and Philip York

It is no good designing a good course if it is not built to the highest standards and it is no good building a good course if maintenance is not of an equally high standard. The three vital processes are inextricably linked.

The role of a good contractor:

1. Researching every project carefully in order to familiarise himself with the site and specification, so that he can price accurately and competitively.

2. Interpreting the specification for the green plans or other working drawings accurately in close liaison with the architect.

3. Maintaining efficient co-ordination of the day-to-day operations.

4. Having the organisational skills to adhere to programme dates.

5. Having experienced and trained staff to cope with all the specialised facets of construction.

6. Working safely and responsibly throughout.

7. Taking pride in the quality of the end product.

The architect may conduct the orchestra but the contractor has to play the music!

Construction

There are many lessons to learn on construction, many starting with architecture. "Use the land you are given" is a sound architectural tenet, going back all of a century. Keep it simple, work with rather than against nature. Obey a few simple

Raquel Carriedo of Spain during the Tenerife Ladies Open. "Great golf cours design is not just limited to the creation of championship golf courses fc professional tournament play only. The true art comes from making the go, course enjoyable and challenging for golfers of all standards. Modern thinkin, and enhanced standards has meant that forward and ladies tees are to k integrated with the entire strategy for any green shot or hole.
Tim Lobb of Thomson Perrett and Lobk

constructional rules and do it right first time, using proven standards and methods and time-tested materials. Fev golfers can resist the temptation, given the opportunity, of designing and building their own course, yet ignoranc combined with optimism makes this the most expensive present they could ever give themselves. Perhaps nowher more than in construction does it pay to learn from the expensively acquired experience of others, be it a multi million extravaganza or a cheap and cheerful farmer's glory. Furthermore, if you do consult an expert, check tha he really is one. What is his track record, what is said by satisfied (or dissatisfied) clients, and even if he is a brilliant designer, has he equally brilliant backup in all the specialist aspects of construction, drainage, irrigation and ecology?

Above all else, remember that golf course construction is more of an art than a science, and that analyses can do nothing to ensure success, only to measure failure. Use common sense, time-proven methods and materials, avoid gimmicks and short-lived fads and, whenever possible, seek the advice of those who have done it all before. They may not have seen absolutely everything, but very little will come as a complete surprise to them.

It is an unbeatable recipe, but commercial pressures make such intimate hour-by-hour supervision, seven days a week, financially impossible – and too many of those designing courses today lack basic agronomic training and education in grasses. Ability to hit a golf ball out of sight and with reasonable accuracy is no substitute for an in-built flair for good design, coupled with a willingness to learn from the experience of others and proper respect for the traditions of this Royal and Ancient game.

Drainage

All in all, since golf is played on many other sites than the ideal light sandy soils of heath or links land, drainage is still a far more important factor, in relation to all-year-round play, than almost any other consideration.

Kingsbarns designed by Kyle Phillips. An extraordinary creation; a great golf course in stunningly picturesque countryside. Designed from flat farmland, constructed to the highest standards with sophisticated irrigation and drainage.

The rules are simple, perhaps the most important one being to drain deep and back up the main system with subsidiaries, mole ploughing, or deep aeration. Uniformity of falls is vital. Falls can be minimal if not imitating a roller coaster drive. Remember, a good system can last for more than a century – and some have lasted even longer – so it pays to take sound advice and go to someone who has done it all before. Modern machinery greatly simplifies and speeds up installation, but there is no substitute for a sound plan supervised by an experienced drainer.

The first rule of drainage is to find an outfall, otherwise the only solution is pumping. The second rule is just as important: employ a skilled and experienced drainer. One is installing a system which may last a century and more, so planning is never wasted.

Irrigation

Water on a golf course should be used as a servant, and never allowed to become the master. We play golf on grass not colour. The chase after the great god green has ruined many of our traditional courses, but thankfully nature is very forgiving and recovery from all but the most irreversible mistreatments is often gratifyingly rapid.

Temple GC – A properly managed irrigation system should encourage deeper rooting and not change the character of the golf course

Temple GC – Hand watering can be of benefit, even with the most sophisticated irrigation system

Remember the old adages. Cold wet greens start growth later than cold dry ones, when growth eventually starts. Water sparingly, little and often.

Vary levels of irrigation according to need, not just on a day by day setting of the timers, but by adjusting arcs of spray and giving some greens more and others less, according to perceived need.

If you have wall-to-wall irrigation use it sparingly and never, never over-water approaches (which is why they should always be quite independently controlled in relation to the greens), as this ruins the run-up game.

Furthermore, remember strict irrigation control is a key to controlling Poa annua invasion, and allowing a return to the bent/fescue turf so characteristic of all our best courses.

Finally, remember that even under ideal working conditions, the best pop-up system can cover turf uniformly, but only uniformly, and most contoured golf greens do not want uniform coverage, but some method whereby low places get less and dry places more. It is pointless merely increasing duration times and volumes, because the dry place stays dry and the wet areas get waterlogged. The answer, at any rate so far, is to top up the dry areas by hand-held hose, with penetration where necessary aided by slitting and the use of wetting agents.

Above all, someone has to control golf club members, who, because they feel they have paid for the irrigation, they and they alone should decide how it is to be used. It should also not be overlooked that in times of water shortage the club's licence for extraction can be restricted or withdrawn at 24-hour notice!

★More detailed information can be found on construction, drainage and irrigation in **"Practical Greenkeeping"**, by Jim Arthur.

Chapter 13

Pity the Poor Golfer ... Safety on the Golf Course ... Golfer and Greenkeeper

By Jon Allbutt
Health and Safety Consultant

Jon has been involved in amenity and industrial horticulture for over 40 years, including a 6 year period in the pesticides industry as a technical development manager for sports turf products. Jon is currently Principal Consultant of Jon Allbutt Associates, health, safety and environmental management consultancy with over 20 years advisory and consultancy experience in the sport and leisure industry.

Like many (ex) greenkeepers who are also golfers I am a true hypocrite! When working on a golf course I longed to be able to work uninterrupted. Those precious hours before the course opened, peaceful with just the sound of my mower and no call of 'Fore' – ignored of course!

OZZY

The practice swing, scattering golfers and their kit!

As a golfer how often have I stood frustrated by the sight of a greenkeeper oblivious to my presence – not really, just ignoring me- as he appeared to frustrate my attempts to reach that elusive target – the green.

How often, too, have I, the golfer, resolved to get to the course early and calmly, full of composure and purpose. I will practice my putting, hit a shot or two in the nets; read the notice board, chat to the pro, sort my kit out and plan my game. But too often it is the mad dash along the narrow lanes clogged with slow traffic, horse riders and pedestrians all pre-warned of my mission impossible!

And then there is the course, my own or another, with its changing moods, different ground conditions, pin positions, temporary greens – not to mention the weather!

In all of this there is the considerable matter of the Rules – another failed resolution! – and not just The Rules, but Local Rules, Dress Codes, New Trees, Irrigation Covers, Paths and Water. Ah yes, the water!

We live in a litigious society these days, seemingly with endless opportunity to sue for the smallest slight on our game, honour, self or safety. Now, speaking of safety, just how safe is a golfer, a golf course, or a greenkeeper for that matter? Is the game actually bad for my health, not just my mental health!

We must not mock he who rides in a buggy for he may be exercising his rights under the Disability Discrimination Act, or is it just another toy?. I am an old fashioned golfer who would rather carry a half set of clubs than give in and pull a trolley, so you can imagine how I feel about buggies on the golf course. As an ex-greenkeeper I loathe all forms of such means of transporting persons and clubs but would not hesitate to use my ride-on mower rather than haul a flymo – hypocrites all! How many golfers are heard to whinge in the clubhouse "We have a trolley ban but the bloody greenkeepers are riding all over the place!"

I learn that I have a Duty of Care to my fellow man – and he to me – and I to the Club, the course – and they to me again. We mustn't do anything to put each other at risk or cause injury. This Duty also extends to taking care, thinking of what we must, and must not do. The Club must distinguish between 'natural features' and 'constructed features' e.g. bridges, steps, etc. But are we the golfer, like all sportsmen, not expected to accept the degree of risk inherent in the sport and the extent to which we might contribute to our own demise?

GOLFERS COMMON SENSE 'RULES' FOR SAFE AND CONSIDERATE PLAY.

One of the most common accidents involving golfers is that old favourite, the practice swing. I have often stood beside good golfers and the occasional professional who shake their heads in amazement at a huge practice swing totally inappropriate for the shot required scattering companions in all directions, and followed by a totally different shot!

Choose your footwear with care; have you checked the condition of your spikes lately? Are you sure those soft spikes give you sufficient grip in poor ground conditions?

Show courtesy and respect for the golf course, your companions and others, and make sure you know the Rules, e.g. did you know that you could be disqualified under Rule 33-7 for lack of etiquette?

Make sure you know the golf course and if you need to give way to a party of walkers, horse-riders or a family group having a picnic in the middle of the fairway!

Visualising your next shot and rehearsing it in your mind are vital to avoiding the dreaded miss hit; but do remember to have a look around for hazards before actually playing the shot!

Choose your route from tee to green – the direct route may not be the safest and can end up with a poor imitation of skiing a Black Run!

And above all, please replace your divots and repair your pitch marks!

CONSIDERING THE GREENKEEPER.

The greenkeeper has as many bosses as there are members, all of whom are experts in greenkeeping. He patiently listens to members offering totally daft, apparently expert advice.

He is criticised for being in the way but also nowhere to be seen during the day – he can't win.

He is considered to be a fair target for the bad tempered golfer, who would never dare play a ball at another golfer.

To present your golf course at its best he must be a psychologist (those members again!), agronomist, ecologist, economist, expert on the Rules, and always produce the perfect golf course just weeks after our televisions have filled our senses with the glory of yet another perfect course - and that after a cold, wet spring.

We do not consider often enough that he is actually there to prepare the course for us and is not keen to be 'in shot' at all, so please wait a moment to allow him to do his job.

Wairoa Golf Club, New Zealand. A wonderful natural 18-hole golf course where members exercise their disability rights by using this unique mode of transport! But this would not be acceptable in the UK because of current Health and Safety regulations.

Chapter 14

The Wildside of Golf

By Dr. Keith Duff
Director of English Nature

Keith Duff is the Chief Scientist, and a National Director of English Nature, the government body responsible for wildlife protection in England. Keith is a member of Toft Hotel Golf Club, where he was Club Captain in 2003. Keith is deeply committed to the environmental aspects of the golf industry, and works closely with both The R&A and the English Golf Union to help achieve this. Between 1997 and 2002 he was one of the judges for the annual BIGGA Golf Environment competition, which gave him the opportunity to experience at first hand the excellent environmental work that is being done on numerous golf courses across Great Britain.

"Keith - Is this a golf course or a Nature Reserve?"

As recently as ten years ago, if you'd asked the average golf course Secretary or manager what they thought of environmentalists (especially those working for organisations which have statutory powers over what happens on some golf courses), you probably wouldn't have been able to print their reply! I know, because I've been on the receiving end of them! The popular perception used to be something along the lines that conservationists are lefty, bearded, sandal-wearing interfering busybodies, with no idea of real land management.

It wasn't ever really like that of course, and *most environmentalists know that golf courses are good for wildlife. Equally, the golf industry is now much more aware that wildlife is good for golf courses.* The recent creation of The R&A's website promoting good environmental management of golf courses is clear evidence of this. In this contribution, I want to explore the mutual benefits, and summarise the key things that golfers and golf course managers need to know about.

The UK has comprehensive and powerful environmental legislation, part national and part derived from the EU. In England, 105 golf courses lie wholly or partly within SSSIs (Sites of Special Scientific Interest), and the overall UK total is in the region of 250. Under law, anyone wishing to change the existing management practice on an SSSI, or carry out any land use changes or development, is required to consult the relevant statutory organisation. They will consider whether what is proposed will damage the features for which the site was designated, and have the power to refuse consent for any such activity. Pretty draconian stuff, potentially.

In practice, though, such obstructive decisions are very rare. It is the roughs that are of interest to nature conservationists, not the tees, greens and fairways, and sustainable management of the roughs generally produces what both golfers and ecologists want. On links courses such as Royal St Georges, Rye, Saunton, Royal Birkdale and Silloth, the rough grasslands on the dune ridges provide major challenges to the golfer whose tee shot fades

Royston GC, Hertfordshire, the delicate Pasque Flower is one of Britain's rarest and most spectacular native plants. The largest population in the UK is at Royston GC where over 30,000 plants flower every year.

too much, but also comprise important habitats which are now rare in Britain, and which contain diverse assemblages of wild flowers, butterflies and birds. Indeed, if links courses hadn't been built a century ago, it's likely that much of the land they cover would have been built on, or covered in caravans! The same applies on heathland courses such as Hankley Common, Broadstone, Walton Heath and Sunningdale, where the heather roughs are the essence of the golf course, and wonderful habitats for wildlife. Indeed, in all these cases, there is a close relationship between English Nature and the club, which works to our mutual advantage.

The 105 golf course SSSIs in England cover about 6500 hectares, and are an important part of the SSSI estate. Forty-two of them are so important ecologically that they are also given protected status under EU environmental law, through the EU Habitats and Birds Directives. EU protection is even tougher than UK protection, but conflict between nature conservation and golf course management is still rare. This is shown particularly well by the fact that two of the four English Open Championship venues (Royal Birkdale, and Royal St Georges) are European protected sites, and there have been no insurmountable difficulties in agreeing spectator management procedures, siting of the tented villages, and course preparation.

What conservationists don't want to see is the roughs being watered or fertilised, as this changes their ecological character quickly and substantially. Again, this is usually entirely in keeping with what course managers want. *Spending money on water and chemicals for use in the roughs isn't exactly good for the club's cashflow,* and also has a tendency to increase plants such as nettles and course grasses, which makes ball finding harder, and increases the risk of unwanted grass species invading fairways and greens.

There's a further shared interest too. Water availability is likely to become more problematic in the future, as climate change leads to water shortages, particularly in the south of England. Wetlands are already suffering from low groundwater levels, and there will be increased pressures on clubs to reduce their levels of water usage. Course managers are often aware of the desirability of using water more sparingly, and optimising the presence of more appropriate local grass species on fairways and greens. But the "Augusta effect" has led to pressures from many club members for courses to be greener, which is neither ecologically nor "traditionally" desirable. Historically, most links courses (for example) would have had summer fairways which were much barer and browner. *There is an education and awareness issue that needs to be addressed here, which relates also to the need for ongoing management of the roughs to prevent them being invaded and overwhelmed by scrub.* In the past, this would have been prevented by the effects of grazing animals, but this has now almost entirely ceased, with the result being that many links, heath and parkland courses are losing their original character. *Periodic radical management is necessary to restore them, but is often resisted by members who are wary of such change.*

Many examples exist of how English Nature and SSSI golf course managers work well together, to mutual advantage. For example, Royal St Georges needed to construct several new tees for the 2003 Open Championship, all of which were located within areas of ecologically important rough included within the SSSI and European protected site. Building from the good working relationship developed over several years, and with some small scale tweaking and the provision of mitigation works in other parts of the site, English Nature was able to agree the proposals. Other examples include large scale clearance of sea buckthorn scrub at Burnham and Berrow, restoring the traditional links feel of the course, and large scale clearance of creeping willow scrub at Royal Birkdale, to the same effect. On inland courses the same has happened, with extensive scrub clearance at Lindrick, to restore the open grass heaths on this historic Ryder Cup course, and massive pine clearance at Hankley

Common, to restore open heather environments on this classic Surrey heathland course. ***In several of these cases, English Nature provided a financial contribution towards the restoration management.***

There are, it must be said, rare occasions where the existence of a statutory designation does create problems. The most difficult in recent years has probably been at Royal West Norfolk Golf Club, on the North Norfolk coast at Brancaster. This famous links course sits within a European protected site for its coastal and dune habitats, and is sandwiched between the sea, which periodically causes erosion of the dune frontage to the course, and a European protected site for birds behind it. Sea level rise, as a consequence of long term climate change, means that there will be continuing challenges for English Nature and the club to address. In such cases, the important thing is to ensure that dialogue continues, with the aim of achieving an agreeable resolution. In the meantime, the "soft coast defences" installed a couple of years ago seem to be working pretty well at the moment.

To ensure that our officers have a sound understanding of the golf industry, the way that courses are managed, and our corporate policy towards golf course management, English Nature periodically provides a 3-day training course for our local officers who are responsible for managing our relationship with golf clubs. This is led by two senior English nature officers who are both golfers (myself and Tom Tew), assisted by Bob Taylor from STRI. We include visits to golf courses as part of this, to meet club officers and employees, and to see examples of good management being done. English Nature's policy on golf course management is appended to this piece, but in summary it:

- recognises the benefits of golf courses

- supports the industry in improving environmental performance

- commits English Nature to providing clear advice and objectives, and some financial support, where appropriate, for habitat restoration

Royal West Norfolk Golf Club at Brancaster, sandwiched between Internationally important grazing marshes and an important marine site.

- makes clear that playing surfaces are generally not of concern to English Nature

- stresses that it is the non-playing areas which are generally important for wildlife

These examples all relate to the English situation, but similar activities and approaches also operate in Scotland and Wales. The equivalent bodies to English Nature – Scottish Natural Heritage and the Countryside Council for Wales – are also committed to working closely with the golf industry, especially on SSSIs and European sites. As in England, there is commitment from the top of the organisation to ensuring that satisfactory outcomes are achieved.

Scotland led the way in developing an ecological advisory service for golf clubs, through the establishment of the Scottish Golf Environment Group, funded jointly by Scottish Natural Heritage, the Scottish Golf Union, and The R&A. This provides an excellent service to all clubs, and has led to real advances in the environmental quality of golf courses in Scotland. A comparable system was set up in England in 2002, jointly funded by English Nature and the English Golf Union. This provides a free ecological advice service to golf clubs (both SSSIs and non-designated sites), and is delivered through the Sports Turf Research Institute. Since its inception it has been massively oversubscribed, which is a powerful indication of the levels of environmental interest within golf clubs in England. Consideration is currently being given to the establishment of a similar system in Wales.

Over subscription to the English Nature – English Golf Union initiative demonstrates that it's not just the "special" sites which are important. The landscape of lowland England is now so fragmented, as a result of agricultural intensification and built development, that the special sites themselves are at risk of becoming isolated islands unable to function ecologically, as there is no connection with adjacent or nearby sites. Inbreeding and gradual loss of species is therefore a growing risk. This means that the wider countryside between these special sites becomes even more important, especially those parts of it which still retain areas of semi-natural habitat – and that includes golf courses. Many of the 2000+ golf courses in England contain important patches of habitat that support good populations of wildlife, and which also act as "ecological stepping stones" or corridors between protected sites. So they form a vital part of the ecological fabric of England, and one that will become more important. Many courses, such as Temple Golf Club in Berkshire, contain extensive areas of good habitat, which define the playing character of the course. The management of their large areas of hay meadows provides a vital ecological oasis, rich in orchids, butterflies and skylarks, and also provides an unforgettable experience to members and visitors.

Increasingly, courses are providing members with more comprehensive information about what's happening on their course, both in terms of course maintenance and management, and in terms of information on what wildlife they can see. Some courses, such as The Dyke near Brighton, have wonderful displays of photographs of the wildlife on the course, which enhances the experience and appreciation of everyone.

Major championships also provide great opportunities for raising the environmental profile of the golf industry. For several years now, The R&A has produced (in partnership with English Nature, Scottish Natural Heritage, the Environment Agency, and other bodies) beautifully illustrated hole-by-hole guides to the wildlife and conservation features to be seen on the Open Championship venues. These are distributed free at the championship, and enable thousands of people to appreciate exactly how much of a contribution the golf industry is making to the environment. They also provide the BBC TV commentary team with information that is broadcast to millions of people across the world – who can forget the slow zoom in to a skylark or a lizard orchid, accompanied by Peter Alliss' pithy observations!

Temple GC – orchids by the 18th tee – one of 5 different species of orchid to be found on the course.

Working together, the Royal St Georges Booklet for the 2003 Open Championship

It's not just the statutory nature conservation organisations which are engaging with the golf industry. There is a growing recognition and acceptance within the voluntary organisations active in the environmental field, that golf course management is beneficial and good for wildlife. This brings potential benefits to clubs, as these local voluntary organisations can often be the source of advice and specialist help, for example in carrying out species surveys of the golf course, as at Temple Golf Club. It also cements relationships with the local community.

Big environmental challenges face us all in the coming years, largely as a result of climate change. These will affect wildlife on golf courses and elsewhere, but they will also have direct impacts on the condition and management of the golf courses themselves. Climate change is already causing changes in rainfall patterns, which have direct impacts on courses, and indirect ones as subsurface aquifers become affected. By working more closely with the environmental organisations, the industry will have access to better information on trends, impacts and potential responses, and will be better placed to develop responses which have more chance of long-term success. Water resource pressures will become more challenging, in part as a result of the EU Water Framework Directive, and the Environment Agency's review of water abstraction consents. Closer working will ensure that integrated responses can be developed.

Hankley Common GC, a fine example of ecological management. The mown heather roughs provide ecologically and architecturally important areas for the golf course.

More and more clubs are recognising the need for long term planning of the management of their business, both with regard to the club itself and to the management of their greatest and most valuable asset – the golf course. It's the character of the course which determines the quality of the experience that we have every time we play. Closer links with statutory and voluntary nature conservation bodies will help with the preparation of strategic course management plans, since such bodies are well-versed in producing, reviewing the updating long term management plans for their own nature reserves, and for ecological improvement at the landscape scale.

There is a powerful alliance already developing between the golf industry and the nature conservation movement, with a great deal of common interest. It is to our mutual advantage to develop this further, and show that golf course management is environmentally beneficial; there are still large numbers of people who see golf as being environmentally damaging. But just stop and think – what is richer in wildlife, intensively managed farmland or a golf course with well managed roughs? There's no doubt in my mind! Even fairways can provide important ecological niches; one of my strongest memories is of seeing woodlarks (a rare heathland species) feeding on insects on fairways at Hankley Common, which shows us that even intensively managed areas of turf play vital roles in the ecological web.

So, my message is a simple one. The statutory nature conservation agencies have a strong awareness of the operation and interests of the golf industry, and understand their needs and aspirations. We believe, and experience supports this, that there is a close relationship between the objectives of nature conservation and sustainable management of the golf course on SSSIs and European sites which lie within golf courses. The best chance for us both to achieve our objectives is by working together, and promoting the good news stories which emerge from this.

Mark Twain got it wrong. Golf isn't a good walk spoiled – it's an opportunity to rise to the challenge of the game itself, and do it in an environment which lifts the spirit. The challenge for all of us is to create and maintain that environment.

Chapter 15

The Commandments of the Prophet

By Jim Arthur
Consultant Agronomist

Royal Cinque Ports GC - A club which has communicated with it's members, and is achieving amazing results.

I can do no better than quote Sir Michael Bonallack:

"For many years, Jim Arthur acted as consultant agronomist to the Championship Committee of The R&A, ensuring that courses for each Championship were played in the best possible condition.

However, Jim Arthur has never believed in compromising long term standards for short term presentation and thinks just as much about the ordinary golf club members' needs as he does about those required for players in the Open Championship.

Invariably controversial, but infuriatingly nearly always right, Jim Arthur's knowledge about courses and greenkeeping is probably second to none."

Sir Michael F. Bonallack, O.B.E.

Many involved in golf at all levels, not just in greenkeeping, have agreed that until the golfer can be educated into understanding what greenkeeping is all about, we are wasting time and effort in trying to improve not only many of our courses but the game itself.

Very few golfers ever get seriously involved in course management. The few that do can have a disproportionate influence on their courses, for bad as well as good. Some run their courses on semi dictatorial regimes. One example comes to mind – the 'permanent' chairman of the green committee of a famous links course, used to address his new green committee to advise them that "by the constitution of the club, we have to elect a green committee. I give you notice that we meet once a year for dinner and you do not have to attend. I run the course and so long as it is in good order that's the way it will be! Your job is to keep the members off the greenkeeper's back".

Sadly amiable dictators working on sound lines are scarce and should be cherished, but they eventually have to be replaced and therein lies the problem almost always the discontented element changes policies diametrically, just for the sake of it. Hence the cyclic pattern of disaster and slow recovery.

For most clubs it seems that management tries to please members rather than to implement sound consistent long term policies designed to produce the best possible conditions for as many of the 365 days a year that weather permits.

Three quarters of a century ago it was commonplace for our maternal ancestors to add a generous spoonful of bicarbonate of soda to cooking vegetables as it gave the greens a bright green colour. It took 50 years of dieticians' advice that this totally destroyed the nutritional value of the vegetables and to stop this practice with its unintended consequences. Today's golfers have yet to be convinced that their bicarb, i.e. over use of fertilisers and water in pursuit of colour, destroys all year round golf.

Of course, they are seduced by televised tournaments and glossy press, when even a hint of anything other than lush green attracts adverse comments. I do not know which is worse, that the advocates of this 'green is great' school do not realise the consequences long term in both course condition and the serious impact on budgets, or they are aware but are happy to accept the consequences.

If the average golfer could absorb the unarguable case for better all year round condition based on greenkeeping principles that have not altered since time, let alone golf, began, then we would not face so many disasters or huge remedial costs.

Greenkeeping is essentially an art not a science. It is based on botany, not soil chemistry and very little to do with soil physics. It is not ruled by scientific formulae, soil analyses or learned academic research. It is a study of a very few grasses. Good greenkeepers are natural conservationists. They rely on accurately guessing in advance weather patterns and other natural phenomena. Apart from luck (essential in all husbandry) they base their plans partly on following very simple rules and partly on experience, which today receives very little credit. They know well in advance by interpreting signs – we call it field experience – when action is needed. They balance the needs of the golfer against those of their grasses – and if they shout that danger looms, they must be listened to.

Greenkeeping is a study of basically two good grasses and a few bad ones. No prizes for the chief contender for the latter title – viz annual meadow grass. The good ones are the fine fescues and bents (Agrostis) but not all of the strains of each. We play, or should play if we wish to follow the precepts of the Royal & Ancient game, on fine firm, crisp, weed and worm-free turf, not on colour. Colour is inescapably linked with that dreaded and ubiquitous weed (Poa annua). It is widely acknowledged as the enemy of good greenkeeping and the source of 90% of all greenkeeping problems.

Even those who praise Poa annua admit its faults – bad surfaces, thatch formation, soft sappy growth, prolific seeding in even close mown turf, disease and wear susceptibility, very poor winter performance (after all it is a short-lived annual). Admittedly it is quick to respond to fertilisers and aggressively invasive, so responds to panic remedial measures and soon dominates in response to so-called remedies which were initiated by the failure of this weed grass in the first place.

Why then do we tolerate it with all its faults? The answer is because it takes clever greenkeeping to keep it out and with one mistake it dominates fine turf, and it takes years of hard work to get it out again. One seriously worrying factor is that it is so prone to suffer, not only from drought and wear, but from disease, and whatever the rights of the case we are progressively being prevented from using fungicides both by hostile legislation and by products being withdrawn as demand falls and costs of certification render them commercially non viable. Well-managed courses rarely need to use any fungicide; lush ones use huge amounts.

What then are these principles on which greenkeeping for centuries has passively – and in the last century actively followed? ***The clue lies in nature – good greenkeeping copies those conditions where natural grassland is dominated by fine wiry turf.*** Such environments are very varied. They range from contrasting acid moors and heathland to alkaline downs and links; from light sandy impoverished soils to worn out heavy clays; from free draining sands (links and heathland) to totally flooded by the sea at high tides.

One might wonder where the common ground exists between such diverse ecologies – yet common ground there must be as it is undisputed that soil and the natural conditions decide on the character of the flora which is dominant on any land, rich and poor alike.

Those conditions are quite simple. All the soils are infertile – too low in plant nutrients to be farmed and indeed actually toxic to farm grasses. Such low nutrient status may be enforced by leaching (washing out plant foods in thin free draining sands etc.) or by acidity – locking up nutrients demanded by other more lush and demanding species which therefore cannot compete against poverty tolerant species. Drainage must be good and so soils must be uncompacted. Traffic causing compaction and damage before actual erosion starts, brings in annual meadow grass, colonising the compacted soil because deeper-rooted grasses are penalised.

We do need to aerate deeply and regularly – however much this upsets members. Properly done the interference lasts only a few days. One greenkeeper chided by members who was told to stop aerating the greens, replied, "Certainly, providing you stop playing on them!"

Member: Stop aerating the greens.

Greenkeeper: "Certainly providing you stop playing on them!"

OZZY

To develop this precept it is important that all should accept that basic principles of both the game and of greenkeeping have not altered in centuries, yet some pundits are always trying to change the rules. Sadly most have little or no scientific training or even practical experience, though a few do know but shamelessly "prostitute science to commerce". Most of them naturally are the proud owners of lush green lawns.

As evidence of the long standing problem of presentation (as exemplified by target versus pitch and run golf) I quote from 50 years ago, from his book on the History of Golf by a famous golfing editor Robert Browning. He points out so well the differences still evident today, describing the Ryder Cup of 1953 at Wentworth, between the British contenders and their American opponents. The first pair played the hole (the par 4 13th at Wentworth) "perfectly in the way the golf architect who designed it, intended them to do". The Americans adopted an entirely different school of tactics, viz straight down the middle of the fairway with their second shot dropping four yards from the hole, stopping stone dead. "The British pair played

I think you have overdone the water!

OZZY

that hole with the perfection of artists, the Americans with the precision of machines. And in the long run the artists will always be beaten by the machines". Or so he claimed! We have been so keen to take the element of chance out of the game that we have destroyed the test of the ability of each man to stand up to bad luck, a rub of the green.

What the advocates of target golf fail to stress is that to achieve the aim of stopping near the flag, one needs tight lies on close knit, fine, firm turf in order to apply back spin. With lush turf — especially ryegrass — that is impossible. With a ball lying down in a verdant meadow, especially if grass blades come between the ball and the face of the club, the inevitable result is a flier. With soft greens, the ball plugs, though more likely it will scuttle across and off the green because it has had no back spin on it, being played out of a lush lie.

To achieve high all year round standards of play – on incidentally much lower budgets – we need to use water and fertiliser sparingly. Start late and finish early with both. Such naturally managed courses need not be seared or parched, but we must eschew lush verdant vegetation and favour bents and fescues. Never chase colour – but until someone with ultimate discipline and control stops turning their back on the problem and lays down the law to uneducated golfers to change their indoctrinated or instinctive reactions, greenkeeping education is wasted. Too many good greenkeepers are forced to give up and give the majority of members what they want rather than what they should have, if they want all year round golf on low budgets.

The rot started with Bobby Locke, four times Open Champion but like most (not all) professionals, no greenkeeper. He played on necessarily heavily irrigated American courses which had to contend with high temperatures and drought. He was attracted by the possibility of playing for the flag and not just to the green. He did not realise the dangers of introducing such policies into cooler and wetter climates – especially in areas with long wet though not <u>very</u> cold winters, where golfers <u>wanted</u> to continue to play all year round.

Keep them mean and rely on those native grasses which give us such good courses by realising that they grow on the poorest (but well aerated and free draining) soils. This is a plus for those meeting increasing financial problems – such natural management costs much less, gives inherent disease control and prevention and produces far better all year round results for far less money.

The brutal fact is that in the coming increasingly financially difficult years, only sound austere low budget management will stop more courses deteriorating or actually closing in winter. Let me stress however that traditional greenkeeping does not mean old fashioned. ***Such methods proven by centuries of practice and a century of research as well as implementation cut costs by avoiding or anticipating and preventing problems such as disease.***

Good greenkeepers really do think of their members, getting up long before dawn to keep out of their way. They may have to do unpopular things or risk losing their course, but they do expect and deserve understanding from their members and freedom from criticism that they are not implementing irrelevant American ideas. Sadly some have given up the fight and settled for a quiet life giving vociferous but ill informed members what they want.

Chapter 16

The Grass is Always Greener, or is it?

By Peter Wisbey
Courses Manager, Woodhall Spa, The National
Golf Centre of the English Golf Union

The Algarve Pinheiros Altos GC – where the greens are mown for 365 days a year.

Peter Wisbey entered greenkeeping in 1966. Starting as an apprentice at North Foreland G.C., Broadstairs, Kent. He was promoted to the position of Head Greenkeeper in 1970, and was Course Manager from 1975 until 1987.

He moved to Portugal in June 1987 to complete the construction and grow - in of San Lorenzo. Peter then managed San Lorenzo and the 36 holes at Penina until 1991, when he was asked to complete the construction and grow - in of Pinheiros Altos. From 1993 until late 1996 Peter managed Pinheiros Altos and the original 36 holes in Quinta do Lago.

In December 1996 Peter returned to the UK at the invitation of the English Golf Union, to oversee the renovation of the World renowned Hotchkin Course at Woodhall Spa, presently rated number one inland course in England, and the grow in of the new Donald Steel designed Bracken Course.

Early in the 1980's at North Foreland Golf Club, Kent. The Assistant Professional approached me as I was passing by the Pro Shop. 'Mr K is very unhappy with the greens', he told me. This was early in April and, as any Greenkeeper will tell you, two things are certain at this time of year. Firstly the U.S. Masters appears on our televisions; an immaculate course with smooth, fast greens and, secondly, our own courses are at a low ebb. For most of us, the various species of grasses in our greens start growing at different ground temperatures and therefore, the greens are uneven and slow.

So. I wasn't really surprised by these comments. Never happy to hear of discontent, I approached Mr K as he was packing his clubs into the boot of his car. I gave a brief explanation of why our greens were not at their best, when he replied 'that's all very well, but last week I played on some beautiful greens! 'Oh,' I thought, wondering if this was at Royal St Georges, Deal or Canterbury? How could they achieve such conditions when I could not? A little self-doubt started to creep in. His answer to my question of where left me almost but not quite speechless. 'The Algarve'. 'Was it hot?' I enquired, 'oh yes it was beautiful' he replied. 'Don't you think that that makes a difference to the growth of the grasses on the courses out there?', 'I don't know , why should it? If Mr K had voiced these opinions in the clubhouse without mentioning that he had been playing abroad, unfair pressure would have been put on me, the Greenkeeper.

I am sure many Greenkeepers over the past 20 years will have been criticized for the condition of their courses in general, and the greens in particular, at those difficult times of year when British golfers head for the sun during winter and early spring – some to the United States or South Africa, and others much nearer to home, Spain and Portugal being the most popular.

It never ceases to amaze me that seemingly intelligent people cannot make the obvious connection between weather and course condition.

The reason Malcolm asked me to contribute to this book is that in 1987 I was offered the opportunity to move

Home of the English Golf Union, the Hotchkiss Course, Woodhall Spa

The Grass is Always Greener, or is it?

to the Algarve to complete the construction and subsequent grow-in of an absolute stunning golf course, San Lorenzo. I can, therefore speak, with the knowledge gained from managing courses in both northern and southern Europe. Separated by two and a half hours in a plane, they are worlds apart in terms of turfgrass husbandry.

The Algarve does have a winter, but not as we know it. Night-time temperatures can drop to zero and frost does form in some sheltered corners. However, the daytime temperatures, following such a night-time low, can reach the low twenties, ideal for short-sleeved shirts and shorts, whilst at home it's body warmers, woolly hats and gloves.

The first twenty-two years of my greenkeeping career was spent, as already mentioned, at North Foreland Golf Club situated on the chalk downs close to Broadstairs in Kent. Perfect land for golf – come late April growth was underway and by mid May surfaces were true and smooth. Since my return from Portugal in late 1996, I have been fortunate to manage the two courses at Woodhall Spa in Linconshire. Home to the England Golf Union, under three hundred miles further north than North Foreland, but what a difference in our growing season. We are probable a month behind those courses in the south east of the country and, of course, the southwest will be even further ahead. How many golfers realize this when discussing and, yes, criticizing courses?

Returning to the warmth of the southern part of Europe, not only is the climate different, but in most cases so are the grasses used on the courses. Invariably the greens are sown with Agrostis Stolonifera, or to give it's better known name, 'Creeping Bent', a vigorous grass, the latest cultivars of which have been developed in the United States, that does well in a warmer climate. Some courses in the U.K. have used various cultivars of this grass with varying degrees of success. The majority becomes infested with Poa annua or 'Annual Meadow Grass' quite quickly. The few courses that have been able to maintain a pure stand do so at no little cost to their membership. They either hand weed Poa annua plants or, at least in one case, relay the greens completely, which is prohibitively expensive.

Although creeping bent grows well in the heat of the south it is, in fact, a 'cool season grass'. Do not confuse 'cool' with 'cold'. Whereas in our climate the grasses grow between April and late October, in Spain and Portugal they grow strongly all year round. *In fact, greens are mown 365 days a year. That's right, Christmas Day as well!* The very fact that the grass is growing means that it is constantly repairing itself, disease scars, pitch marks and any other surface imperfections soon grow over. Whilst back in the cold U.K., the scars of the Fusarium attack suffered in October will still be with you in March/April the next year. The increase in winter golf in this country adds to the wear and tear on what is, effectively, dormant turf.

More and more enlightened clubs are carrying out their major renovation work in late summer rather than late autumn. Such works include scarification, hollow coring and Vertidraining. As the turf is actively growing the holes and grooves left after such operations heal rapidly and you enter the dormant period with smooth surfaces.

When a committee decides that such works must wait until after the competition season, sometimes through October and into early November, they will, invariably suffer thin, bumpy greens throughout the winter and early spring. Do they then take the inevitable criticism on the chin? Of course not! The greenstaff haven't done their job correctly, are incompetent or worse. Am I being harsh or unfair? Unfortunately not. Many good, skilful and honest turf managers are being lost to our profession yearly and at an increasing rate. Some are dismissed; others simply cannot take the stress any more.

Comparisons between courses are inevitable. Competition between the same courses regarding condition and presentation is healthy and keeps us all on our toes. But, please, be realistic. Compare oranges with oranges and apples with apples.

No one can control the weather but the weather does control us. Air temperatures relate directly to soil temperatures. These are the key to all we do and all we can achieve. As mentioned previously, in southern Europe it does get cold at night, but the daytime highs mean that the soil temperatures rarely drop below 12°C enough to keep the grass growth ticking steadily along. We may not see these temperatures until after Easter. *A good rule of thumb is to look at the trees on the course. Until they are in full leaf your greens will not be at their best. Ground temperatures remember, are the key to everything that grows in the soil. It is this that governs when and how things grow, not a fixture list!*

Chapter 17

Golf's Doomsday in Europe – It could happen to us

By Chris Haspell
Course Manager, Hørsholm GC, Denmark

Chris started working in sports turf in 1983. When he maintained bowling greens, tennis courts, and cricket pitches. In 1989 he fell in love with golf, when building Oaklands Golf and Country Club in Cheshire. In 1995 he moved to Denmark to work at Falster Golf Club, and was soon invited to advise other golf clubs in the area. In 1999 the Danish Golf Union approached Chris to be their consultant and he now advises over 150 clubs in the country.

With the support of The R&A, Chris is producing a handbook on the best ways to maintain a traditional fescue sward.

Picture the scene. It's the middle of September in 2010. You arrive for the monthly medal, and as you make your way to the first tee the anticipation of a good round is almost too much to bear. The greens are incredible, cut low and very fast, they look like a billiard table. As you walk off the 18th with your 36 points, you anticipate an even better round in next weeks club championship. You have a wry smile, pleased that you encouraged the Chairman of Green to arrange for the greens to be cut

The risk of Poa annua: Fusarium attack on Poa annua green in Northern Europe, where fungicides are banned.

even lower. In the meantime, unbeknown to you, government has imposed a ban on fungicides to start from midnight. The lobby was made in Brussels in 2005.

During the week you go to the club to practice for Sundays Championship, but the greens have changed, brown patches and small indentations have appeared on the surface. "Oh well, the Chairman of the Green will kick the greenkeeper, who will then spray them before the Championship, everything will be ok on the day.

Sunday arrives, and rumours have been flying around about the poor condition of the greens but you know it cannot be true. You play the first hole and reach the green, 40% of the grass cover has disappeared, what's going on? After 10 holes you are ready to give up, the Chairman of Green will surely be roasted after the Championship.

In the clubhouse the talk is tough: sack the Committee and, the Course Manager. It is of course their incompetence, which has led to the poor condition of the greens. The new committee convenes, and, following policy reads the minutes of the last year's meetings. "What's all this about fungicide restriction? It goes back 5 years, why have we not been informed?"

The fact is we probably have, but our own arrogance gives us the 'it will never happen to us' syndrome. Poa annua (annual meadow grass) has been in golf greens for years. Management practice and the pressure of TV golf have driven down the cutting heights and increased the demand for colour, thus promoting Poa, The problem is that Poa is the grass type most susceptible to fungal disease. If spraying pesticide is illegal there is a big problem. Poa is also susceptible to drought and can be devastated by disease brought on in wet conditions. Is the perception of emerald green worth the heavy watering and fertilising?

For me this is reality. I have been working in Denmark for 10 years, and we were informed in 1995 that in 2003 there would be no chemicals available. Many courses now have these restrictions but it is up to each individual county to decide whether spraying is allowed in their area (that's like giving the power to your local council). Even if permission is granted to spray there is only one fungicide available, and this is useless unless you have exactly the right temperature, and even this is expected to be banned soon. Coupled with restrictions on water and tax on nitrogen we did not have many options other than fescue/bent-dominated surfaces. These bans are not confined to Denmark, they also exist in Norway, parts of Germany, and the Netherlands.

Denmark is a relatively new golfing nation with the oldest course being 104 years old. It is by design a target golf nation with most of the influences coming from the States. All golfers like to have emerald greens and stop the ball easily. There are only a few golfers who appreciate the subtlety of pitch and run golf with firm fast greens. Not because they do not have links or heathland conditions but because management techniques since the 60s have favoured Poa annua, and, subsequently, soggy surfaces. During my time as a consultant in Denmark I have seen several good examples of Poa greens and there is no doubt with lots of chemicals you can maintain a good sward. However, after the restrictions, it is all too often the case that these types of greens are only in decent condition from about May, and start to decline at the end of September. This will only get worse without any fungicides.

But it is not all gloom and doom. We have some shining examples of greenkeepers and golf clubs, which changed their policy. They have dominant fescue sward, which they mow at 5mm - 6mm and still produce fast, true greens. Unfortunately the colour seems to effect peoples opinion. After a recent professional tournament near to Copenhagen I gave a presentation, to about 30 of the pros, on golf course management. After asking about the greens at the competition which were running at 10.5ft on the stimpmeter (Editors Note. This is the green speed requested for The Open Championship, weather conditions are taken into consideration. Trueness of roll and good health are more important than just speed at The Open Championship) I was told that they did not like the greens. "Why?" I asked. They could not stop the ball quickly enough, so they had to adjust there game, was their response. They thought the greens looked funny. I delved deeper "Were they true?" Yes, was the reply. "Were they quick?" Yes. So what was the problem? After an hour's discussion they all agreed that they were as good as any greens they had ever played on, they were just not used to the colour and texture. "Would they like more of these types of greens?" Yes, how do we achieve this? By changing the golfer's perception of colour and quality. If you have ever played on a good fescue sward and, let's face it, not many have, it's like playing on a big light yellow/green 'brillo pad' but the trueness when putting is fantastic.

Many people say that fescue cannot become dominant on old Poa greens but this is nonsense. The problem is that even consultants advise a softly-softly approach and in many cases do not know what to recommend or to look for in a return to fescue/bent. Many even say look after the Poa, especially the fertilizer salesman/consultants who are used by a misguided committee or greenkeeper to save money for the club, a saving that invariably costs a great deal more in the long term. We have a "pay and play" course just outside Copenhagen that has 54 holes, both short and long courses. The main course has in excess of 60.000 rounds a year and still maintains fescue even with winter play. All fairways are fescue, all greens are bent and fescue mixture, so the cynics who say it can't stand traffic, are wrong. It is the cutting height that needs to be changed. Many sceptics will not believe these claims but Jack McMillan from the European Tour and Steve Isaac and Nick Park from The R &A have all witnessed this first hand.

On my previous course we have reintroduced up to 80% bent fescue domination over the last ten years. We have around 40 - 45.000 rounds a year. It's a parkland/woodland course, with greens, which generally run at 8.5 – 9 on the stimpmeter (see glossary of terms). On a daily basis this is cutting at 5mm but with a light verti-cutting and topdressing programme. The key to success is low fertilization, primarily light dressings of 8.0.0 throughout the season and around 40-60 kilos of nitrogen in an average year. Keeping the surface as dry as possible for as long as possible, we try to give the Poa "cold turkey" with a fine balance of watering to maintain a surface but enough to encourage drought stress on the Poa and keep it on the back foot. Obviously this was difficult at first with high-domination of Poa on the greens. As someone once said to me, it's like changing the engine of a car while still driving. On top of this we use seaweed approximately once a month and a little K (potassium) in the last dressing which normally comes in September.

In Great Britain you only need to travel to golf courses like St Andrews and talk with Gordon Moir, or to Kingsbarns where Stuart Mccolm deserves a medal, to Birkdale where Chris Whittle is reintroducing fescue and doing an excellent job. It's not just championship golf courses either; Martin Gunn at Temple has produced a wonderful course, for natural golf with a high percentage of fescue in the fairway and a bent and fescue mix in the greens. Also Gordon Irvine who is helping Royal Cinque Ports restore the great links at Deal.

We need to change golfers' perception of how a green looks, and get them to focus more on how it putts. Change the way they play into the green and learn that the green should not accept a thinned four iron from 150 metres. We also have the problem of lost knowledge and management techniques. So let's harness the experience we have left before it's too late!

What of the future of golf in the UK? In my opinion a spraying ban will also hit the UK, probably within 10 years. In terms of the life of a golf course this is a very short and Mother Nature needs help to work with you. Things will not change overnight. To put the political situation into perspective, Denmark is at present sitting on the environmental seat in Brussels, so my forecast will not be far wrong. Of course, in any project you need the backing of your club. If you explain these facts (not fiction) to your Committee and members, they will look a little more at the long term and give you the chance to try and re-introduce fescue and bent. What's the alternative? Greens, infected by the disease fusarium, which will not recover until the middle of May or even June and fall in quality towards the end of September, that's a five month season! Will the golfers accept that?

The facts are that a strategy needs to be in place now to try to achieve a higher percentage of bent and fescue on the greens, get the cutting height up, and change the management programme. This will not compromise quality, in fact just the opposite. For all the clubs that don't, the future is a fall in quality and revenue and maybe worse, as golfers seek those courses which have been better prepared. I am the first to admit you will never be 100% Poa free, but with Poa in the minority there exists the possibility of quick true greens and a sustainable surface for the next 100 years.

(Editor's note: Chris's article deserves serious consideration ... Because if he is right and many authorities in golf course management think he is. Golf clubs need to be considering their future today!)

Chapter 18

It's not a miracle –
it's down to skill!!!

By David F Golding
Education Director, The Greenkeepers Training
Committee (GTC)

David Golding represented his county at golf, aged 16. He had to choose between becoming a Golf Professional or a Greenkeeper. He chose to become a 'Professional Greenkeeper'.

David's green-keeping career took him from Buxton and High Peak Golf Club to Camberley Heath Golf Club, Surrey before returning north to Dore and Totley Golf Club, Sheffield. Finally, he was Course Manager of two municipal courses in Manchester.

In 1989 David joined the British & International Golf Greenkeepers Association (BIGGA) as the Association's full time Education Officer and in 1993 he was invited to front an Education Unit to be funded by the four

Bill Patterson, Course Manager, Beaconsfield GC, who went to evening classes to become computer literate.

Home Unions, The R & A and the PGA European Tour. The Greenkeeper Training Committee came into being, with David Golding as Education Director, representing all golf clubs and greenkeepers to influence all aspects of greenkeeper education and training.

His thought - provoking chapter should leave us all asking a few questions of how we golfers always think the condition of the course is down to the weather if it is in good condition or the greenkeeper if it is below standard!

How many of you golfers could name the greenkeeping staff at your club? Many golfers do not even know the name of their Course Manager! The greenkeeping "team" who work to ensure your chosen leisure time is as enjoyable as possible really are a friendly crowd. "Why should I know their names" I hear you ask. Well believe it or not greenkeepers truly care about the condition of the course 24 hours a day 7 days a week. Keeping the customer happy 365 days a year is a very difficult job. It can also be a very lonely job especially in the depths of winter or in a drought period just prior to the clubs major event of the calendar.

It is amazing how a golfer, just by passing a polite "good morning the course is looking fine" can spur a greenkeeper on and make them feel that their efforts are appreciated.

True, they are employees of the club, but the majority of people entering the profession of greenkeeping are a unique breed! Who else would sign up to a Job Description that includes :

1 You will carry out instructions from person(s) that know absolutely nothing about your line of work. The number of persons may vary from time to time but can be up to 700!

   NB The majority of these people are "qualified" as they have gardens of their own and as turf is often an integral part of the garden never question their advice!

2 When the course is in excellent condition the "recent rain" will be given the credit but any other times you will take full responsibility for any criticism of the course.

3 Never approach the winner of a competition to ask what they thought of the course – breach of this rule could lead to disciplinary action!

Sorry, to be a little tongue in cheek but these are points that sometimes "hurt" the greenkeeper when they always are striving to maintain the standards now being demanded by the golfer.

So, let us take a serious look at the role of the greenkeeper and Course Manager.

The Course Manager, yes Course Manager I believe to be the most important person employed by the golf club. Everything that happens at the club is supplementary to the playing of the game and that is not to undervalue the clubhouse activities, the vital role of the Secretary/Manager, Professional, Steward etc.

The majority of people join a golf club primarily to play golf and therefore the priority MUST be the course. The course has to be maintained and managed therefore there has to be a person responsible for this happening on a day to day basis. In all industries specialist knowledge and skills are required. Why then, in golf course maintenance are the specialists recommendations too often questioned by the "unqualified?" Today's qualified Course Managers are multi-talented people whose wide-ranging skills are only appreciated by employers who have taken the time to research the profession.

The game has moved into a difficult period in the United Kingdom with a proliferation of new courses being built during the 1990's and many clubs desperately trying to hold onto members whilst at the same time attract visitors. Never has there been a better time to employ a qualified Course Manager! The greenstaff will be motivated by the Course Manager through ongoing skills development, and, arguably just as important the committee will be able to concentrate on other matters rather than being concerned on matters other than everyday issues that clearly fall within a Course Managers remit.

The number of times I read Green Committee minutes and to my horror see such trivial matters discussed seemingly for hours, I think that if a Course Manager were employed the committee would not even know of such occurrences! The role of a Green Committee, is through consultation with its Course Manager to develop and maintain a Golf Course Policy Document incorporating Health & Safety and Environment policies When clearly defined, this is the only way forward for any type of golf club. It must be a "live" document, - But once it approved it must be adhered to, and a change of Chairman or Course Manager should not normally require any changes to the policies. All too often have we seen Chairman's folly: the new tree planted or tree felled – the new bunker constructed or filled in etc etc! Greenkeepers are not exempt from this type of radical action either – changes to the course should never be left to "one man's whim".

There are, of course, the owner/ proprietors who can do what they want to their course but, again, so many problems are created by not employing a qualified Course Manager. Skill plays an important role in the playing of the sport but, equally, it is the skills of the greenstaff, which produce the surfaces.

Golf clubs must ensure staff are given the opportunity to train and receive the support to maximize their potential in accordance with the club's required standards.

The Course Manager should be the person entrusted to implement the club's agreed policies for the course, but he, like any manager, is only as good as the "team". Many Course Managers are now qualified trainer/assessors, which not only enhances their own profile but assists staff to develop their personal knowledge and skills. The opportunity for greenstaff to gain formal qualifications has never been greater now that the colleges are

It's not a miracle – it's down to skill!!!

Tim Brooke-Taylor – "Student greenkeeper" photographed to promote greenkeeper education for the GTC magazine "On Course".

offering a range of courses with different delivery methods.

The majority of U.K turf students now study "on the job" with support from their Course Manager and chosen college. Vocational qualifications are now available in the sports turf sector and these are mainly delivered at the golf course.

The more academic qualifications are available through landbased colleges and these can be either completed on a part or full-time route. It is a very wise employer that invests in its staff and, fortunately for golf clubs the bodies in the U.K established to represent them have developed a structure to deliver education and training, which is fully in line with the Government's policy.

The education and training of greenkeepers cannot be an option for any golf club. The only decision any employer has is how formal should the training to be?

However, with the emphasis on skills training never has there been a better time for golf club employers to assess their staff's training requirements and this can either be carried out in conjunction with their Course Manager or invite a GTC Approved Training Provider to visit your club to discuss individuals' training needs.

Thankfully this trend has now improved through greater awareness of the education system by the "customer". Golf club employers often through their Course Manager now monitor students' progress far more closely and in turn benefit from a more skilled and motivated workforce.

At least once a year employers should be carrying out a full staff appraisal with monitoring of training progress on at least a quarterly basis.

So, next time you walk to the 1st tee please spare a thought for the "team" of greenstaff who have prepared "your" course for the day and by the time you walk off the 18th green you might have enjoyed your game shot a 59 and truly do believe that miracles can happen!

Chapter 19

The Future – Take Golf Back to it's Roots

By Tom Mackenzie
Golf Course Architect

Tom Mackenzie is a golf course architect of 15 years experience who has worked extensively throughout Europe, as well as the USA, Canada and the Caribbean. To date he has 30 new courses under his belt. He is a keen category one golfer who has been a member of Royal Dornoch Golf Club for more than 20 years. He was a member of the main committee and chairman of the green committee at a previous club, which gave him valuable insight into the workings of a golf club.

I have written this as a golf course architect since 1989 and as a golfer with some direct and indirect experience of golf committees and all of the frustrations that that involves.

In the early days of the 20th century, a new school of thought took root in British golf called strategic design. It formed the basis for the design of almost all of the great courses in the world. It is a simple theory: that the players who think their way around a course should receive greater reward than the player who uses raw power. The best holes are, therefore, designed like miniature chess games that tempt, test and tease all standards of player, but those tested the most are the best players, who are more up to the challenge. The reverse is also true, or as Tom Simpson once said, "poor players carry their bunkers with them".

Strategic golf works best when conditions are firm and dry because the little humps and bumps are exaggerated in their importance. The softer the conditions are, the more players resort to aerial bombardment and these features become largely irrelevant. This is the main reason why there has been a trend in recent years to create courses with gimmicky features, such as island greens, vast lakes and bunkers and with greens that are cut tighter and tighter every week. They are all ways to introduce rewards for accuracy, but the results crucify the average player. The old courses were designed for subtle play, but if they are soft and squidgy, then much of the architect's original intent is lost. The new courses are far less subtle, some would say crude.

So, what relevance does this have to greenkeeping? The answer is "a great deal" because it shows how closely linked golf course design and greenkeeping are. A hole with water directly in front of the green soon becomes unplayable if the green is as hard as concrete and a great strategic hole soon loses much of its greatness if it is presented in a soft and spongy condition.

All too many committees and golfers have no appreciation of the connection between turf health and course presentation. On too many occasions, greenkeepers have little choice but to succumb to the enormous pressure applied by ignorant individuals and groups and make the course "nice and lush" as instructed, albeit against their better judgement. When this ill-considered stance results in turf problems and disease, it is justified because it can be treated chemically. The chemicals are approved and the logic is therefore that they are there to be used. But, what if the chemicals are not there?

It may come as a surprise to some that all fungicides are already prohibited for use on golf courses in parts of Germany, Scandinavia and Holland and the trend is bound to continue. In Britain, virtually every form of effective worm control has now been banned and this year sees the banning of another important insecticide.

At least one course in the States, Vineyard Golf Club on Martha's Vineyard, Massachusetts, could only gain planning consent by agreeing not to use any inorganic substances on the course, so the use of pesticides is prohibited. Only organic fertilisers can be used and there are dozens of ground water monitoring points all over the course. The club has to pay for independent scientists to test water regularly and the results are then sent to the local Conservation Commission which has the power to close the course if the commitments are not met.

On such courses, there are few alternatives to traditional greenkeeping methods. Fertility levels have to be closely matched to minimise damaging bouts of disease and, more importantly, the members have to be educated to expect

Aerial view of the Vineyard Golf Club, Martha's Vineyard

conditions which are not peaked too often as the more grass is abused, the more susceptible it becomes to disease and decline.

The story returns to the Vineyard Golf Club and its water monitoring. One year after the course opened, there was a big scare locally when a neighbouring property found excessive nitrogen levels in its well water. Immediately a furore broke out with all and sundry instantly pointing the finger at the course as the polluter. The water monitoring results saved the day, however, as they proved categorically that the course was not guilty. Further investigation proved that it was contamination from a nearby septic tank; not a pleasant thought. It was, however, a classic case of golf being guilty until it proved itself innocent. Ask yourself why the game has to do this.

Science also has a big role to play in the future. New strains of grass are being bred that have vastly improved disease and drought resistance. This may or may not involve the introduction of genetically modified grasses but there has to be a major question mark over whether such grasses would simply make golf courses more distrusted by the environmental lobbies. Other advances are being made on biological controls, whereby diseases are controlled by introducing different fungi into the soil. These will certainly help to maintain standards, but it is likely that established courses will suffer before they improve and significant investment has to be expected.

It is almost inevitable that this article will prompt many in the golf industry to yawn and say, "Here, we go again, the same old stuff. Haven't we moved on?" The answer is that matters have not moved on. The luxury of chemicals is a relatively short-lived one and has allowed the time-proven rules to be bent too much. Whatever the rights and wrongs of people's perceptions, the reality is that for golf to continue to prosper, offering all that it does to the young and old alike, the management of the courses has to change.

There are many courses that have been built on heavy inland soils with greens that were specifically designed to retain water and the future without chemicals for these courses is gloomy. There will be little or no alternative but to rebuild all of the greens so that they perform better all of the time. In many respects, improved fungicides have allowed these courses to defer the inevitable decision to rebuild. Modern golf involves so much winter play that it stands to reason that greens built to retain water are rarely going to perform satisfactorily year round. That some do is more a reflection of the skill of the greenkeepers and agronomists than the construction.

This has an immediate impact on design as well. For those addicted to the constant diet of television golf on courses dominated with sand and water and set up to be "nice and green and stripy", a rude awakening awaits, especially in cooler climates. Courses will have to become firmer as restrictions are imposed, particularly on water abstraction. This will mean that courses will have to be designed for running golf, with open approaches and few, if any, forced carries. This is the type of golf that is the mainstay of British and Irish golf, but it is increasingly under pressure, with many golfers simply not appreciating its heritage and importance or its practical and affordable approach.

Another aspect to consider in all of this is that of the impact of new clubs and balls on the game. This has long been the Achilles heel of the game and is a subject, which the administrators have been unable to control for the past century or more. We are assured that all is under control now, but few share this optimistic view. In all likelihood, the ball will continue to fly further and further. The difficulty is that in Britain and Ireland nearly 60% of the courses are less than 6400 yards long and only 10% are longer than 6700 yards. Most of the former are stretched to their limit with no room to accommodate extra tees.

The best and, all to often, the only way for courses to defend themselves against new clubs and balls is to strengthen the strategic test that the course presents. Many have bunkers that are isolated in the rough as fairways have been narrowed in response to the "new" game and they will be moved on and into fairways so that the best players are forced to flirt with them to gain positional advantage.

When the list of top 100 courses in the UK and Ireland is analysed, it is amazing how many old courses designed by the likes of Colt and Fowler feature almost unaltered after 70 or 80 years. The

Fortrose and Rosemarkie. A traditional Scottish links, managed to traditional principles results in a fine test of golf allied to good stewardship of the coastal environment.

answer is that these gentlemen were the fathers of strategic design and they were relentless in forcing all players to think their way around from first tee to last green. Not all courses were designed to such a high standard, but these principles still dominate the thinking of traditionally minded architects. The dimensions of the game may have changed since the 1930s, but the basic principles of good design have not.

An associated problem in years to come will be litigation and the trends are already there to see. It is difficult for clubs to stomach that they are entirely responsible for ensuring that, under normal play, their course does not cause a safety problem to neighbours, but the law could hardly be clearer. There are countless examples of courses being redesigned because balls are hitting a new house or road that is built hard up against the boundary, even though the course has been there for a century already.

New clubs and balls may help the best players to hit the ball further and straighter, but they are not quite so helpful for the wilder hitters who merely hit the ball further off line. In coming years, clubs should buy any and every piece of land around their boundaries that comes available, at virtually any price. So many clubs have regretted turning down opportunities on the grounds of expense, only to face far greater costs of redesign later. One famous club even sold adjacent land for housing, thus creating a safety problem.

In conclusion, can the game do anything about all of this? This book is a good starting point, but those reading it are probably already far more enlightened than most. Playing major competitions on courses that set a good example would, of course, help, but the commercial reality of professional golf is that most events are played on the course that is owned by the highest bidder. How sad it is that Europe insists on playing successive Ryder Cups on courses that so few like but that fit nicely with the third grass, third water, third sand formula. There is not much chance of change there, though.

The R & A help to promote the natural game through publishing books and videos, but their coverage up to this point has been small because they have had little direct access to the average golfer. Their recent moves of establishing a golf course committee with a full time coordinator is an ambitious step forward but the scale of the task is enormous. Perhaps their most important role, though, is to bring technology finally under control. The commercial might of the manufacturers makes this far from easy but the game continues to do itself a huge disservice by failing to impose more effective control. After all, it is the members that have to pay up to alter their courses to try to keep pace and many courses have reached the point where little can now be done.

Controls on chemicals will come sooner rather than later, whether we like it or not, and greenkeepers and members alike must adjust to what that means. In many instances, reconstruction of the greens will be essential to give the grass a chance. More research on new grasses and biological controls will help and it is encouraging that much of this is ongoing and funded partly by The R&A and USGA. *Somehow, though, average golfers need to have their perceptions changed of what they consider to be a course in good condition.*

Televised golf is disproportionately influential in this regard, but it is hard to see what can be done about that. Golfers just have to be reminded over and over again why their course is set up as it is. It is certainly an uphill struggle but those clubs that have done best in this respect are those that have brought their head greenkeeper or course manager into the front line, through information evenings and other gatherings. This is certainly not everyone's cup of tea, but somehow the "us and them" attitude that prevails at many clubs has to be broken down. It is not a one-off process, either, but an ongoing one, given the constant turnover of committee members and the short-term thinking that that invokes.

There is no reason to be gloomy, though. The game is poised to move forward. Better turf will result from the gradual banning of chemicals, but the interim period may well be painful for many. The sooner that the pain is over and done with the better the game shall be. It will mark a return to the game that so many love.

Chapter 20

The Last Piece in the Jigsaw...The Role of The R&A

By Steve Isaac.
Assistant Director –
Golf Course Management The R & A.

Steve joined STRI in 1985 working in the research department. In 1986 he moved to the agronomy division working in eastern England, followed by 9 years in Scotland. He was agronomist to The R&A for the 1999, 2000 and 2002 Open Championships and the 1999 Walker Cup at Nairn.

In May 2003, Steve took the post of Secretary to the Golf Course Committee at The R&A. He is responsible for helping to develop the Committee's programme and enacting its decisions. The Committee was established to provide guidance and help on all aspects of golf course management. Although its span is worldwide initial activities are concentrating on the needs of federations and unions within Europe and the Committee's main objectives are:

● The provision of the best-practice guidelines for course management.

● The co-ordination of research.

● The promotion of the game's interests through political and environmental bodies

Steve is a 14 handicap golfer who plays most of his golf on the links of St Andrews.

The call

The R&A has, for many years, taken a keen interest in the golf course. After all, without the golf facility there would be no game. Whilst the Rules, Championships and Equipment Standards tend to take centre stage in R&A affairs, the golf course has never been neglected. Publications such as "The Way Forward" and "A Course for All Seasons" have outlined our philosophy on golf course, and golf club, management. However, it was a conference in Portugal that saw the amplification of The R&A's role in relation to the golf course.

At this meeting in November 2001, European Golf Associations called on The R&A to give a lead in matters such as:

● Teaching and encouraging best management practices on golf courses.

● Promoting environmental and ecological care.

● Co-ordinating research into reducing chemical use.

● Adapting to the consequences of climate change.

● Conserving water, and placing the game of golf in the forefront of exemplary community planning.

The meeting also called on The R&A to support and influence EU legislation.

Peter Dawson, The R&A's Chief Executive, responded immediately to this call and formed the Golf Course Committee, which first sat in May 2002. The objectives of the Committee were defined as:

● The provision of best practice guidelines for course management.

● The co-ordination of research.

● The promotion of the game's interests through political and environmental bodies.

The vision

The first major step in fulfilling these objectives was taken in February 2004, when The R&A launched one of the most ambitious projects it has ever undertaken - an interactive website providing Best Practice Guidelines for course management, www.bestcourseforgolf.org

The development of the website fulfils Peter Dawson's vision: "The challenge for golf is to maintain course quality and playability while respecting and positively contributing to the social and natural environment".

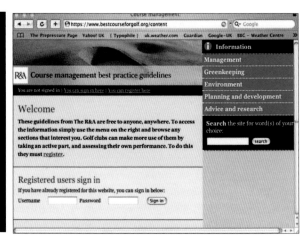

The Website: Course Management Practice Guidelines

This vision and The R&A's response to the call in Portugal reflect the increasing demands of environmental obligation and economic pressure on golf course development and management across the world. Remember, The R&A is responsible to all of its 127 Affiliates and not just the four home countries of GB&I.

Developing and working the website

The website can be viewed free of charge by anyone anywhere by accessing www.bestcourseforgolf.org

There is a secure construction within the site which allows golf clubs to register and put the guidelines into practice through a series of checklists. Clubs can allocate responsibility for completing the checklists in the main sections of text – Management, Greenkeeping, Environment, Administration, Planning and Development – to nominated employees or members who have the most appropriate skills in these fields. It is our hope that by working through the checklists and producing documentation supportive of actual implementation of best practice, clubs around the world will display a clear willingness to operate in harmony with the environment.

In addition to prompting action in relation to working to best practice, the website provides all those registering to the site with the option of signing up to an email user group, a useful forum for exchange of ideas, problems and experiences.

There is a helpful user guide to the site, which is available as a pdf file which can be downloaded or printed off. This explains how the site works and covers the process by which registered clubs can add users from within the club to progress through the checklist programme.

The purpose and response to the website

It is hoped the website will suit many purposes – a means of supporting course managers and their committees; an education tool for all those directly associated with course management and those who play the courses; a source of persuasive information for legislators and environmental activists that golf courses are a sustainable form of land management which can make a positive contribution to our natural heritage.

By 2005, over 1000 clubs from 80 different countries had registered to the site, with 10% having started working the checklist system. The Golf Course Committee is delighted with this response but emphasise that the site will evolve as more information comes on stream and material from other avenues of our work and in response to user feedback, which is very welcome, is incorporated. It is intended to review site content twice a year, the initial review being completed in July 2004.

As part of this review process, a series of case studies on sustainable management of golf courses is being developed. The R&A Golf Course Committee has travelled extensively round Europe to uncover working examples which complement the best practice guidelines and fulfil our definition of sustainability:

"Optimising the playing quality of the golf course in harmony with the conservation of its natural environment under economically sound management".

The future

www.bestcourseforgolf.org provides The R&A with a clear focus for its work in relation to golf course management. The website expounds the fundamental principles of sound greenkeeping which were documented in "The Way Forward" and "A Course for All Seasons", and provides a platform to develop and disseminate supportive information to a global audience. Future work of the Committee will concentrate on developing this information so that anyone, anywhere in the world wishing to work to best practice has the backing of The R&A and all other organisations supporting the site.

By working the website and implementing best practice, clubs all over the world will demonstrate that golf is a sustainable user of land. This has to benefit the development of the game globally and, provided the message is broadcast successfully, should ease the concerns of governments and environmental organisations which may not yet take this view.

The R&A, through the best practice website, demonstrates that golf courses can be managed sustainably, without conflict with environmental or economic concerns. This is the essence of 'natural' golf, a game which fits in with the environment, with courses managed in sympathy with nature, resulting in an affordable and rewarding experience.

"The need for best practice is global."

Mount Merapi GC, Indonesia – designed by Peter Thomson.

Chapter 21

A Golfing Craic

By Terry Wogan OBE
Radio and Television Presenter

Peter Alliss, Terry Wogan, and Lee Trevino during BBC's Pro Celebrity Golf

Terry was born in Limerick, Ireland. He worked for the Irish National Radio and Television service. In 1967, Terry joined the BBC. He was asked one day to stand in for Jimmy Young and after that, was given a regular afternoon slot. His TV career started with Blankety Blank. In 1982, his life took a new turn, with a Saturday evening chat show entitled "Wogan", which ended up being transmitted live three times a week on BBC 1 for a staggering seven years. Terry was elected "Outstanding Radio Personality of the past 25 Years" He attracts a huge audience of over 7 million, and is undoubtedly the most listened to presenter on radio in the UK. Ask Terry to sum up the secret of his success as one of UK entertainment's top personalities and he replies," I put it down to clean living and plenty of roughage". He was delighted to be awarded an honorary OBE in the1997 New Years Honors List, His autobiography "Is it Me" was published in September 2000, went straight to No 1 in the best sellers and stayed there for many weeks.

After all the agronomy and aggro here's Terry to remind us of the reason we all love golf. Terry's story is typical of how many of us took up the great game of golf. But not all of us have been lucky enough to play with so many golfing greats and on so many wonderful golf courses.

A Golfing Craic

I can't remember how old I was but I was certainly a fresh faced eager young bank clerk, when I first took up the old golf sticks and headed for the nearest green sward. I don't know where the aforementioned sticks came from, possibly my old man got them in a boot sale, I certainly can't imagine that he bought them from a reputable pro-shop.

There were no " Golf-shops " then; **nobody** ever got measured for a club. Razor-blades was what my clubs were; hickory shafted, rusty headed, perished grip razor-blades. I played with them for at least three or four years, a damned sight better than I play now.

I didn't join a club for years, paying my green fees to churn up the courses around Dublin, Newland, Edmonstown, the Castle, and further afield in Skerries and Balbriggam. It was many years before I felt myself ready for the challenge of the great East Coast Irish courses. Portmarnock, Baltray, Royal

"It's not the wind that worries me - But Wogan is playing today".

Dublin what magnificent links! Home to the greats of Irish golf Christy O'Conner, Harry Bradshaw, the legendary amateur Joe Carr. As maturity took its relentless course, I was honoured to be a made a life member of the superb Lahinch Club on Ireland's West Coast, and smartly discovered that the difficulties of Ireland's East Coast links were only in the h'penny place, when compared to Lahinch with a westerly blowing in from the Atlantic not that the weather is ever a mystery in Lahinch. All you have to do is keep an eye on the goats. If they are out on the course, cropping away, take to the links with confidence. If the goats are sheltering in the lee of the clubhouse go fourth at your peril.

For many joyful, privileged years, I took part in BBC TVs Pro-Celebrity Golf on truly great courses; Gleneagles, Turnberry. I played with the best; Arnold Palmer, Gary Player, Greg Norman, Tom Watson, Seve, Faldo, Trevino, Miller, Jacklin, they never gave me a single tip! Not one hint which was just as well. I saw Tom Watson give Gareth Edwards, the greatest scrum half the world has ever seen, a little coaching on the second tee. After that, Gareth couldn't hit his hat.   They don't play the same game as us, true pros, which is why I've never had a word of advice from my great friend Peter Alliss no matter how many times I've played with him. No I tell a lie: Alliss did, once, offer me the encouraging words "Give it a crack", he said. Which just goes to show how much he knows about amateur golf. "Give it a crack" the pill would fly off at right-angles, probably, decapitating the lady captain five fairways away!....

I only gave things a crack when I was playing with razor-blades. Now it's a controlled swing with a sophisticated club. Dead straight and fully 50 yards down the fairway. Topped it again!

Bibliography

Arthur, J. H. 2003. Practical Greenkeeping.

Doak, T. 199.. The Anatomy of a Golf Course.

Hawtree, F. 1998. Aspects of Golf Course Architecture

Hunter, R. 1998. The Links.

MacKenzie, A. 1920. Golf Architecture.

MacKenzie, A. 1993. The Spirit of St Andrews.

Park, E. 1990. Real Golf

Perris, J. & Evans R.D.C. 1996. The Care of the Golf Course

Ross, D. 1996. Golf Has Never Failed Me

Royal & Ancient Golf Club of St Andrews. 1988. The Way Forward

Royal & Ancient Golf Club of St Andrews. 1997. A Course For All Seasons

Scottish Golf Course Wildlife Group, 1997. Golf Natural Heritage

Steel, D. 1992. Classic Golf Links of Great Britain and Ireland

Taylor, R. S. 1995. A Practical Guide to Ecological Management of the Golf Course

Wethered, H. N. and Simpson T. 1929. The Architectural Side of Golf

A Tongue in Cheek
Glossary of Terms ...

Aeration – A very necessary and regular greenkeeping activity designed to upset and inconvenience members. It takes a variety of forms e.g. slitting, solid tining, verti- draining, hollow-coring, micro-tining etc.

Agronomist - An infrequent visitor with concern for grass and for the members playing on it.

Alien Species - Not something from Mars, but a plant or animal in an inappropriate environment

Annual Meadow Grass (Poa annua) - A shallow rooted, disease prone weed grass responsible for many of the problems seen on UK golf courses.

Bent Grass (Agrostis spp.) - Not suspiciously acquired, but very necessary on many sites for sustainable year round golf.

Bunkers - Are inconsistent. Bunkers are not meant to be consistent as they are defined in The Rules of Golf, as a hazard.

Changed Management - The result of a more enlightened approach.

Course Management Policy Document - A very necessary ingredient in the pursuit of a sustainable golf course.

Course Manager compared to Head Greenkeeper - Upgraded terminology providing the modern qualified and well-educated manager with the respect he or she deserves.

Environment - On many courses the surroundings in which the game is played just happen to provide a subliminal feeling of well being integral to the enjoyment of the game and challenge it offers.

Fungicide - A chemical weapon sometimes very necessary to repel disease. Should only be used as part of an integrated pest and disease management strategy.

Fescue Grass (Festuca spp.) - The holy grail of golfing grasses coveted by many but cultivated by few.

Golf Ball - Not a social event, but a Feathery, Gutta Percha, Rubber Cored, Two piece etc.

Golf Course is perfect - I played really well.

Green Committee - A group of agronomic laymen drawn from the body of the Kirk to preside over the well being of the course. It should ideally comprise an odd number of members with three being too many!

Green Speed - Not a hallucinogen drug, but a measure of putting or trickling will be practiced on this day! Increasing green speed can be best achieved, by more frequent mowing, increase verticutting and grooming, reduce nitrogen, careful management of water, increase top-dressing, ensure free drainage and access of light and air. NOT just reducing the mowing height!

Greens - Broccoli, Cabbage, Spinach. Not to be confused with "through the green" or Green Committee.

Greens are too fast or greens are too slow - I putted badly today.

Holistic Management - Treatment of the whole rather than the symptoms.

Links - The narrow strip of sand based estuarine land once occupied by the sea that separates the shore from the more fertile lands. Ideal for golf as it supports the poverty grasses.

Lush Grass - Luxuriant, succulent grass. Suitable for football, rugby, and for feeding cattle but not a golf course.

Manicured - The cosmetic treatment of hands, not to be confused with the presentation of the golf course.

Natural Golf Course - A golf course that exists as an extension of the wider environment rather than an oasis of artificiality.

No grass on the fairway - I can't get my 7 wood in the air.

Organic - As derived from living material containing carbon.

Pesticide - An umbrella term for chemical substances used to control pests, weeds and diseases, includes herbicides, insecticides, fungicides etc.

Real Golf - A type of golf promoted by firm well paced playing surfaces capable of sustaining play throughout the year in the UK.

Rough is too long - I want to hit a driver on every hole, because it goes further not straighter.

Stimpmeter - A tool to access the speed of the golf green

Target Golf - A type of golf played on soft holding turf. Attractive to high handicap golfers and tournament professionals but a wholly disastrous agronomic objective.

Traditional Course - Not roast beef and yorkshire pudding, but a golf course with bent and fescue grass.

Thatch - Not a roof, but an excessive build up of organic matter at the base of the turf. It promotes surface softness and shallow rooting through moisture and nutrient retention.

Confessions of a
Chairman of Green

by Malcolm Peake
published by The Sports Turf Research Institute

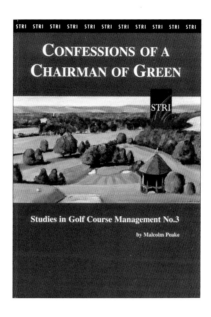

Malcolm's " Confession of a Chairman of Green" is an entertaining and definitive story of how a traditional golf course can work towards its potential.

Christy O'Connor Jnr. Senior British Open Champion 1999 & 2000

Malcolm's book contains a powerful message that less enlightened clubs would do well to heed.

Donald Steel. International Golfer and Golf Course Architect.

This marvelous case study should be read by all those with an interest in good management of golf courses.

Dr Keith Duff. Golfer and Chief Scientist English Nature

Praise for "A Natural Course for Golf"

No other sport enjoys such an intimate relationship with the environment as golf, and many aspects of this relationship are explored in this splendid and long overdue book. It is a fascinating read; entertaining, educational, and of relevance to everyone in the game, from tournament tiger to the club rabbit!
DR ALAN GANGE, SCHOOL OF BIOLOGICAL SCIENCE, ROYAL HOLLOWAY, UNIVERSITY OF LONDON

There is a wealth of sound advice in "A Natural Course for Golf". I recall a phrase from Sir Alf Ramsey, when speaking of Martin Peters playing style during the 1966 World Cup, it also applies to this book " Ten years ahead of its time!"
NICK PARK, VICE CHAIRMAN OF THE R&A GOLF COURSE COMMITTEE

"A Natural Course for Golf" is a unique source of information, which highlights Malcolm's passion for the fundamental principles of sound green-keeping practices. These, unfortunately, are often abused by club committees who listen to members rather than heed accepted policies. This book provides the answer to many golfer's questions.
WALTER WOODS BEM, LINKS SUPERVISOR (RTD), ST ANDREWS LINKS

The English Golf Union places great emphasis on recommending the benefits of good environmental management practices to all our affiliated clubs. Relationships between golf clubs, agronomists, ecologists and conservationists have never been stronger and the benefits are plain to see. The advice contained in " A Natural Course for Golf " is a shining example of the synergy that can be achieved when harmonious working practices are implemented for the mutual and positive ambitions of golf and of the environment.
PAUL M BAXTER, CHIEF EXECUTIVE OFFICER, ENGLISH GOLF UNION

"A Natural Course for Golf" provides a detailed insight into a broad range of golf course management and development issues, and has the potential to stimulate hours of debate amongst golf club officials and members alike. If you want to find out more about golf course management this is an excellent place to start.
COLIN WOOD, CHAIRMAN, SCOTTISH GOLF ENVIRONMENT GROUP.

With more than 40,000 golf courses in practically every climate zone and in more than 100 counties worldwide, it's no wonder that designing, playing, managing and administering the game is unique in every location. Nevertheless, there's a yearning to establish a direction for golf that will ensure a successful future. In this book "A Natural Course for Golf" Malcolm Peake brings together a diverse assemblage of distinguished golf devotees, each of whom reflects on the interrelationships in golf through their own experience and perspective.
JAMES T. SNOW, NATIONAL DIRECTOR, USGA GREEN SECTION.

STRI Golf Course Advisory & Consultancy Services

STRI is the independent market leader in turfgrass research, agronomy and consultancy. It is the UK's national centre for consultancy in sport and amenity turf and a recognised world centre for research.

The STRI's nationwide network of turfgrass advisors and consultants visit over 2000 turf facilities a year, including 1000 golf courses. Our advisory team also provides official agronomy services to The R & A Championship Committee.

STRI offers you a complete service, with independent help and advice, covering all aspects of turf management and maintenance, including agronomy and golf course management, irrigation, architectural and design, redevelopment and renovation, ecology, environmental management, tournament preparation, staffing and mechanisation.

Our golf advisory team are BASIS registered and all highly trained and experienced turfgrass agronomists and specialists. They offer you a unique service which combines practical experience with ready access to state-of-the-art research carried out by our scientific team at Bingley.

In addition STRI also provide testing facilities including rootzone materials, testing for USGA greens construction, disease evaluation, training for Chairmen of Green, Secretaries and Greenkeepers and a mail order and on-line book service supplying over 250 turf titles, an annual Journal of Turfgrass and Sports Surfaces Science and a full colour magazine International Turfgrass Bulletin.

For further information contact our Clients Services at Bingley on **01274 518918** or visit our Website **www.stri.co.uk**